Menta
of the
1991.

mmittee
989 and

The Su
any wa
manus

buted in
ding the

© T

Published in 1992 by:

The Mathematical Association,
259 London Road,
Leicester, LE2 3BE,
England.

ISBN 0 906588 27 8

Printed by Quadrant Press Ltd., Leicester, England
APR 94

Contents

MENTAL METHODS IN MATHEMATICS: A FIRST RESORT

An INSET handbook with ideas for teachers
of children of **all** ages.

The Mathematical Association

1992

1

Two Classroom Incidents

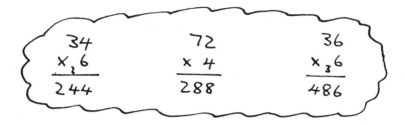

$$34 \qquad 72 \qquad 36$$
$$\times\, 6 \qquad \times\ 4 \qquad \times\,_3 6$$
$$\overline{2\,44} \qquad \overline{288} \qquad \overline{486}$$

David, a student teacher, was observing a first year secondary class (year 7). He noticed Peter who was working on some multiplication 'sums', with the results shown above. On discussing the first of these, David found that Peter's method was like this:

'4 × 6 = 24.
Write down 4 and carry 2.
2 + 6 = 8.
Then, 3 × 8 = 24.
Write down 24.'

Asked about the second 'sum', Peter said:

'2 × 72 = 144.
Then, 2 × 144 = 288.'

The third one was more difficult to sort out, but it appeared that the procedure went something like this:

'6 × 6 = 36.
Write down 6 and carry 3 (or 30?).
3 × 6 = 18.
18 + 30 = 48.
Write down 48.'

Surprised by this mixture of muddled rule following and effective mental methods, David asked Peter to work out 47 × 9. Peter's fairly rapid response, without any written working, was 423. When asked how he had found the correct answer so readily, Peter replied:

'7 × 9 = 63 and 40 × 9 = 360.
So, altogether it is 63 + 360 = 423.'

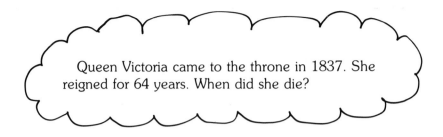

Queen Victoria came to the throne in 1837. She reigned for 64 years. When did she die?

Tony, a pupil in a top junior class (year 6), was working through an exercise with a number of 'problems' like this one, which all involved addition. The exercise was clearly designed to enable children to practise writing down the appropriate sum and then to carry out the standard procedure for addition in order to solve the problem.

Tony had just written:

$$1837$$
$$+64$$

and was about to proceed with 7 + 4, when the following dialogue took place between Tony and his teacher.

'Just a minute. What would it come to, roughly?
Just over 1900.
Why?
Well, 60 + 30 = 90 and 7 + 4 is more than 10, so . . . What is the answer then?
1901.'

The anecdotes about Peter and Tony both involve children practising standard written algorithms to do calculations which they are able to perform mentally with ease and understanding. In the first case, the standard written methods seemed to be a source of considerable confusion to Peter and yet he had sufficient understanding and confidence to be able to devise two completely different ways of calculating the product mentally. In the second case, Tony was at ease with the standard methods, and yet he could do the calculation at least as effectively in his head.

These incidents suggest to us many questions about current classroom practices in relation to children doing calculations at all levels from infant school to sixth form (reception class to year 13). The increasing use of calculators adds a further significant dimension to the issue. The questions on the next page indicate the wide range of issues which we are seeking to explore in the chapters that follow.

★ How do people really calculate?

★ What is the place of **mental** methods of calculation?

★ Should their use be encouraged?

★ What role do they play in relation to understanding?

★ Can mental methods of calculation be taught?

★ Do standard written algorithms have an important role?

★ Is it desirable to understand why they work?

★ Should they still be taught and learnt?

★ How should calculators be used in school?

★ Should they be available at all times?

★ Do they encourage mental laziness?

★ Can calculator use encourage children to do mental calculations?

★ What is the place of talk and discussion in relation to mental methods?

★ How can it be used effectively in the classroom?

★ Do mental methods have comparable applications to geometric imagery and algebraic thinking?

★ Do activities with computers have a part to play in developing mental methods?

Mental Arithmetic in Perspective

Arithmetic

Mental	$\frac{48}{50}$ Above	Very Good
Mechanical	$\frac{43}{50}$ Average	Good

(from a 1952 primary school report)

The Cockcroft Report (1982) commented on the decline in the emphasis placed on mental arithmetic in schools:

> 'Mental arithmetic was once a regular part of the mathematics taught in both primary and secondary schools; very often it occurred as a separate heading in school reports. It is clear that it now occupies a far less prominent position within most mathematics teaching . . .'
>
> (Paragraph 254)

Older textbooks often had exercises which were rigidly divided into the categories 'mental', 'mechanical' and 'problems'. The examples shown on the next page come from Larcombe's Junior Arithmetics, Book 1, a book for upper juniors first published in 1929.

Many readers will recall the mental arithmetic questions which were commonly used to start mathematics lessons in the past, particularly in the primary school. As Cockcroft asserts, it is much less usual to find this in schools today and this has happened for a variety of good reasons, but rarely with any adequate substitute which reflects the widely accepted importance of working mentally.

Two organisational factors are major reasons for this decline. One is the spread of mixed ability classes where the wide range of ability makes it difficult to select appropriate work to challenge every pupil. The other, in part related to this, is the widespread adoption of individualised schemes and the decline of the traditional teacher led class lesson.

NUMBER. Revision

FOR RAPID WORK

A. CURRENT

1. $39 + 28 + 17$
2. $128 + 201$
3. $200. - 73$
4. 25×9
5. 37×8
6. 125×4
7. $213 \div 3$
8. $175 \div 5$
9. $225 \div 9$
10. $427 \div 7$
11. $5 + 25 + 35$
12. $310 - 193$
13. $4 \times 4 \times 2$
14. $5 \times 4 \div 2$
15. $16 \div 4 \times 3$

MECHANICAL

C.

1. $256 + 193 + 128 + 65$
2. $2,100 - 1,654$
3. $400 + 139 - 165$
4. $516 - 408 + 372$
5. $1,000 - 293 - 615$
6. 125×84
7. $3,915 \div 63$
8. $95 \times 16 \div 45$

D.

1. $391 + 108 + 925 + 8$
2. $3,120 - 2,196$
3. $516 + 295 + 84 - 279$
4. $806 - 519 + 1,564$
5. $2,125 - 315 - 296$
6. 231×63
7. $5,124 \div 64$
8. $56 \times 42 \div 49$

X. EASY

1. Write down the number fifteen thousand and forty-six.
2. How many oz. are there in $2\frac{1}{4}$ lb. ?
3. How many dozens are there in 3 gross ?
4. To the difference between a dozen and a score add a dozen and a half.
5. How far shall I go in $3\frac{1}{2}$ hours at the rate of 24 miles an hour ?
6. A boy has 100 marbles. He wins 10, loses 12, and then wins 20. How many has he then ?
7. Write down two factors of 143 and 130.
8. If there are 14 lb. in one stone, how many are there in 2 stone 2 lb. ?

Y. REVISION

1. How many gross are there in 492×48 ?
2. The contents of 16 boxes, each containing 350 cards, are packed equally, as far as possible, into 46 other boxes. How many cards are left over ?
3. A baker delivered 575 loaves and took back 86. How many had he in the van at first ?
4. If 460 oranges are shared equally, as far as possible, among 31 boys, how many does each receive, and how many are left over ?
5. Add together 7 dozen, 8 score, 2 gross, and 8 apples. Then divide the total into 12 equal parts.
6. Divide the difference between 8,622 and 4,899 by 51.
7. 27 lb. are placed into each of 16 boxes, and 37 lb. into each of 14 boxes. Find the total number of lb.
8. In a cask there are 720 herrings. 45 are packed into a hamper. The rest are packed equally into 45 bags. How many are there in each bag ?

A further important factor underlying this decline is an increased sensitivity on the part of teachers to the harm that was done to many children's confidence and attitude to mathematics as a result of the panic inducing effect of mental tests, where speed of response and the competitive element were given undue emphasis. We note the heading 'for rapid work' on the textbook extract on the previous page and a similar emphasis is evident in the advertisement below extracted from the same textbook.

LARCOMBE'S SPEED TESTS in Mental Arithmetic

(for Pupils aged 9-14 years)

These Books are on most original lines.   They provide tests to be worked at the averate rate of A MINUTE A SUM.

They are so designed that all the tests appear on right-hand pages, and the pupil, placing the book on his exercise book, simply writes down the answers in a column.

The aim of these books is to foster great rapidity and accuracy.

Each book contains IN ALL NEARLY 1,000 SUMS.

The Series consists of 5 graded Books for Pupils—Junior I and II. 6d. each net: Senior I and II, 7d. each net; Senior III, 8d. net.

TEACHER'S BOOKS *(with full answers)*, Price 2s. 6d. each net.

EVANS BROTHERS LIMITED
MONTAGUE HOUSE, RUSSEL SQUARE, LONDON

Laurie Buxton, in his book 'Do You Panic about Maths?' (1981), draws particular attention to the emphasis that many mathematics teachers have placed on speed and the effects that this has. Referring to one of the adults, a former head teacher, whom he interviewed during the course of his research, he says:

> 'One of my subjects had as a child been regularly tested on the tables by her father, who demanded instant response. She had the highest level of anxiety and the most rapid entry into panic that I have met. When I got her to do genuine mental arithmetic she believed that she had to answer quickly and was very soon saying, 'I can't, I can't,' and clearly beginning to disintegrate. By luck I struck on the calm phrase 'No hurry' and she managed to complete 15×12 in her head, no mean task.'

(page 7)

The association of mental working with speed seems to be an unfortunate one for many people, although for others it provides a competitive element that they enjoy. If children are to be encouraged to work mentally, speed of response should be seen as only one aspect of the process and not one which is important for all children.

Mental arithmetic is also associated in the minds of many people with recall of facts, where the emphasis is on memory rather than on mental calculation. There are many facts in mathematics, of which multiplication tables are an example, which children should by some stage have committed to memory and be able to recall fairly rapidly. Whether this process of recall is helped or hindered by giving practice against the clock is an open question. Constant repetition through meeting the facts in a variety of contexts may be at least as effective.

However, we are concerned here with what Laurie Buxton refers to as 'genuine' mental arithmetic. If a child cannot remember that 7×8 is equal to 56, then there must be some way of determining it from what is known. The importance of 'genuine' mental arithmetic is that it involves devising strategies for doing calculations, rather than just remembering isolated facts.

John Holt, in his book 'How Children Fail' (1982), spells out how 7×8 is more than an 'isolated fact'.

'But pieces of information like $7 \times 8 = 56$ are not isolated facts. They are parts of the landscape, the territory of numbers, and that person knows them best who sees most clearly how they fit into the landscape and all the other parts of it. The mathematician knows, among many other things, that $7 \times 8 = 56$ is an illustration of the fact that products of even integers are even; that 7×8 is the same as 14×4 or 28×2 or 56×1; that only these pairs of positive integers will give 56 as a product; that 7×8 is $(8 \times 8) - 8$, or $(7 \times 7) + 7$, or $(15 \times 4) - 4$; and so on. He also knows that $7 \times 8 = 56$ is a way of expressing in symbols a relationship that may take many forms in the world of real objects; thus he knows that a rectangle 8 units long and 7 units wide will have an area of 56 square units. But the child who has learnt to say like a parrot, "Seven times eight is fifty-six" knows nothing of its relation to either the real world or to the world of numbers. He has nothing but blind memory to help him. When memory fails, he is perfectly capable of saying that $7 \times 8 = 23$, or that 7×8 is smaller than 7×5, or larger than 7×10. Even when he knows 7×8, he may not know 8×7, he may say it is something quite different. And when he remembers 7×8, he cannot use it. Given a rectangle of 7cm $\times$ 8cm, and asked how many 1 sq-cm pieces he would need to cover it, he will over and over again cover the rectangle with square pieces and laboriously count them up, never seeing any connection between his answer and the multiplication tables he has memorized.'

(page 178)

John Holt's reflections on seven eights draw attention to three inter-related elements that seem to be of key importance in the effective use of mental methods:

★ understanding
★ flexibility
★ context

Understanding

What meaning can we attach to the statement that a child **understands** $7 \times 8 = 56$? Certainly the word 'understand' implies more than simply being able to recall the isolated fact. At the least we might expect an appreciation of the multiplication as repeated addition, as:

$8 + 8 + 8 + 8 + 8 + 8 + 8$

or $7 + 7 + 7 + 7 + 7 + 7 + 7 + 7$

or, pictorially, as the number of stars in a rectangular array:

The child who determines 7×8 by 'chanting' $1 \times 8 = 8, 2 \times 8 = 16, \ldots, 7 \times 8 = 56$ may either be remembering it like a nursery rhyme learnt by rote, or be successively adding on 8 at each stage. In the latter case, the child displays some understanding. However, a deeper level of understanding is displayed by the child who can retrieve the fact more economically by using, for instance, their recall of $8 \times 8 = 64$ to work out 7×8 by subtracting 8 from 64. Depth of understanding is perhaps indicated by the range of links and interconnections a child can make with confidence.

Flexibility

The ability to form such a network of links is a characteristic of the flexible thinking needed to develop and use mental methods effectively. Reliance on standard procedures alone is a hindrance, because the most appropriate method will vary for a particular type of calculation, depending on the particular numbers involved. This is illustrated well by the different methods shown below to find four very similar products.

7×14

$$7 \times 7 = 49$$
$$2 \times 49 = 98$$

7×15

$$7 \times 30 = 210$$
$$\tfrac{1}{2} \text{ of } 210 = 105$$

7×17

$$7 \times 10 = 70$$
$$7 \times 7 = 49$$
$$70 + 49 = 119$$

7×19

$$7 \times 20 = 140$$
$$140 - 7 = 133$$

Context

The third element is the ability to relate numbers and calculations to a context. Many calculations arise from real life situations so that a context is immediately available, but when an isolated calculation is considered, or when the existing context is confusing, the ability to create a suitable context can be illuminating.

To many children $1 - 0.63$ or $2 \div 0.01$ look forbidding and difficult, but if they are related to the context of money, they immediately become much clearer.

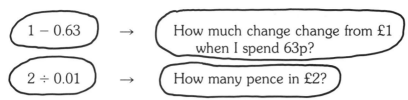

$1 - 0.63$ → How much change change from £1 when I spend 63p?

$2 ÷ 0.01$ → How many pence in £2?

Likewise the use of a picture or objects, real or imagined, often provides a context which clarifies what is required. The teacher can provide such contexts, but it is much more valuable to encourage children to think of their own by asking them to suggest situations which illustrate particular calculations.

Mental Methods in the Classroom

In this book our concern with mental methods is primarily related to doing calculations, although we do give some consideration to geometric imagery and algebraic thinking. We seek to stimulate debate amongst teachers about mental methods and encourage the view that they are an essential aspect of children's learning of mathematics which should pervade classroom activity. This view is spelt out clearly in the section on 'Pupils doing calculations' in the Non-Statutory Guidance to Mathematics in the National Curriculum (1989):

> 'This central place of mental methods should be reflected in an approach that encourages pupils to look at these methods as a 'first resort' when a calculation is needed. Such methods are the basis upon which all standard and non-standard written methods are built, and they underpin a wide range of approaches to calculating.'

> (page E2)

The teacher's personal view of mathematics is a dominant factor in determining children's attitudes and approaches to the subject. If mathematics is seen by the teacher as a matter of remembering and applying a set of standard procedures, then it is unlikely that children will acquire and value the flexible approaches which are the hallmark of the effective mental calculator. However, although a broad view of mathematics coupled with an acceptance of the value of such methods may well be a necessary condition for encouraging their widespread use, it will certainly not be sufficient. There is a need for a range of activities and approaches which are very different from the old exclusive reliance on frequent tests of mental arithmetic.

The Non-Statutory Guidance suggests four ways in which classroom activity can incorporate these methods by giving pupils time to:

★ explore numbers and become familiar with the properties and relationships between numbers;

★ develop a familiarity with addition, subtraction and multiplication facts;

★ consolidate knowledge through purposeful practice of recalling and using such facts in realistic contexts;

★ develop, compare and discuss strategies for dealing with more complex mental calculations.

> (page E3)

Mental methods should be an element that pervades much of children's mathematical work. Opportunities continually arise in the classroom for the teacher to draw attention to particular calculations and use them as a focus for discussion about appropriate methods. We feel that consideration needs to be given, at all levels, to the sort of activities that will stimulate such discussion. ✳

We have noted that flexibility is a key characteristic of mental methods, making it important to encourage a wide range of strategies and methods. This again emphasises the importance of discussion as a means both of sharing ideas and of furthering understanding. In this area children have at least as much to learn from each other as from the teacher. Indeed the teacher who listens will learn a lot too!

The teacher's task is to ensure that plenty of varied opportunities arise which will stimulate this desirable discussion. Often these will arise naturally within work on a range of different topics, but specific activities to encourage mental work also have an important place.

Inset Activities

When we considered how to communicate our ideas to a wider audience, our first thoughts were to produce a collection of classroom material. On reflection we felt that such material already existed in abundance and that a better approach might be to encourage teachers to use more effectively what is readily available. Moreover, we felt that **attitudes** to mental methods were crucial and these are likely to be most strongly influenced by the discussion and interaction that is stimulated by good in-service activities.

In-service education, or professional development, takes place in many ways, both **formally** through courses arranged by LEAs and institutions and through school based activity of different kinds, and **informally** through discussion, working together, observation and reading. We would not necessarily envisage formal in-service courses on mental methods, but would see the topic as one which should pervade much discussion concerning children learning about number operations at all levels. It certainly merits specific consideration through some sessions in a formal course or the occasional staff meeting in a school. However, informal approaches are at least as important. The primary school mathematics coordinator, the secondary school head of department and the LEA adviser and advisory teacher are all in a position to use the odd ten minute conversation to share a relevant experience or point to a useful source of ideas.

For all these categories of in-service activity, we have tried to provide some useful ideas and material. Each chapter includes a number of INSET activities, which are designed to provoke thought and discussion among groups of teachers and to encourage them to try some different classroom activities and approaches. We have not attempted to specify the age range to which ideas might apply, because many of the issues are not age specific and examples at an appropriate level can easily be devised to suit particular children and classes.

In chapter two we ask you to consider what actually happens when children are asked to perform calculations in your classroom and to consider the wide range of methods that are in common use. Any discussion of methods of calculation must consider the place of written methods and we address this in chapter three, where we look at the place of traditional written algorithms and of more informal written methods. In chapter four we consider the role of calculators and how their use can play a valuable part in stimulating mental methods of calculation.

We have given considerable emphasis throughout the book to the need for discussion amongst teachers, between pupils and between teachers and pupils, but effective discussion in the classroom is not easy to achieve. Chapter five addresses this important issue and suggests ways of encouraging effective talk in the classroom.

Mental methods are primarily associated in people's minds with arithmetical calculations. We have included a number of algebraic examples in the book in various places and chapter six is specifically concerned with mental imagery — using mental methods in a geometrical context. In keeping with our view that mental methods should pervade a wide range of mathematical activity, chapter seven suggests some ways in which mental methods can be stimulated by work with microcomputers. Finally, in chapter eight, we draw some of the threads together by reflecting on the frequent plea for schools to go 'back to basics'.

We certainly do not pretend to know the answers to many of the questions that we raise, but we do hope that we can encourage continued active consideration of our view of the importance of mental methods as a 'first resort' in all mathematical work.

2 What Happens in Your Classroom is not what you think!

'Seven times eight'

In chapter one we quoted John Holt's observations on the seemingly simple matter of seven multiplied by eight. It is worth looking further at such a calculation and seeing what it might reveal about our pupils' thinking.

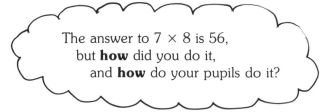

The answer to 7×8 is 56, but **how** did you do it, and **how** do your pupils do it?

Here are the responses of some pupils:

'I just knew it.'

'Well, I know 6 eights are 48, so I just added on 8.'

'I did my eights — 8, 16, 24, 32, 40, 48, <u>56</u>,'
          (on her fingers)

'8 eights are 64, so it must be 56.'

'2 sevens are 14; 2 fourteens are 28; 2 twenty eights are 56.'

'10 sevens are 70, take 14, so it's 56.'

These responses are from a group of **able** students in year 10, students who are in the habit of reflecting upon and sharing their mental methods. What is surprising is the range of methods that they are willing to consider even for solving such a trivial problem.

In this chapter there are a number of activities for groups of teachers to try with the purpose of exploring the diversity of mental methods that children commonly use in classrooms today, with or without the active encouragement of their teachers.

Inset Activity 2:1

53 − 29

Working in a small group of teachers, try to devise as many ways as you can of doing this calculation. Consider formal and informal methods, both written and mental. Someone should record all the ideas suggested on a blackboard or overhead projector.

Compare and discuss the different methods that have been suggested, both in your own small group and with other groups.

★ Are some methods easy to explain orally but difficult to write down?

★ Are some methods easy to write down, but difficult to explain?

★ How do the particular numbers selected for the problem influence the possible methods of solution?

★ Can you suggest other subtractions, involving a pair of two digit numbers, where different methods might be used?

★ Is it possible to group the different methods of solution that have been used in some way?

★ Are some methods more efficient than others?

Try the same activity using other simple calculations. A few suggestions are given below, but you may wish to think of some others to try.

a) 27 + 65   b) 200 − 57

c) 12 × 5   d) ½ of 54

e) 64 ÷ 4   f) ¾ of 96

Reflections

Here are two informal methods for $53 - 29$:

> 'Add 1 gives 30, then 20 gives 50, now 3, so 24 in all.'

> '$53 - 20$ leaves 33, take 3 leaves 30, take 6 gives 24.'

Recording such approaches involves writing down a train of thought, which is not always easy to do clearly, even for such a relatively trivial calculation. Often, an oral explanation is much easier to follow.

Many informal strategies, whether mental or written, will involve either counting up from 29 or counting down from 53. Success with such methods is dependent on a clear understanding of place value and a familiarity with simple addition and subtraction facts.

★   If a child can successfully find a way from 53 to 29 or from 29 to 53 by one such route, is there any virtue in seeking alternatives by sharing ideas with others in the class?

★   Should we seek to promote the growth of such informal strategies in children and if so how should we go about it?

★   How should we respond to a written form like this?

$$53 - 20 = 33 - 3 = 30 - 6 = 24$$

Amongst written methods you will undoubtedly have included the two standard written algorithms, which differ in the way in which they deal with 'the digit on the bottom is bigger than the digit on the top'.

Decomposition: Equal additions:

$$
\begin{array}{r}
{}^{4}\!\cancel{5}\,{}^{1}3 \\
-\ 29 \\
\hline
24
\end{array}
\qquad\qquad
\begin{array}{r}
5\,{}^{1}3 \\
-\,{}_{3}29 \\
\hline
24
\end{array}
$$

★   Can you explain how these two methods work?

★   Can your pupils explain them (or at least the one that they are familiar with)?

★   Compare these methods with mental methods. What are the advantages and disadvantages?

Inset Activity 2:2

Find 60% of £40

All the teachers in the group should do the calculation independently, noting carefully their method of solution. Then all the methods that have been used can be shared by displaying them on a blackboard or overhead projector.

Discuss your reactions to the different methods that have been employed. These questions may assist your discussions:

★ What would you hope for or expect from your pupils?

★ Does the 'niceness' of the numbers influence the method used to find the solution?

★ Is there a 'best' method?

★ Why might some methods be described as 'lazy'?

★ Why might others be described as 'neat' or 'elegant'?

★ Actively seek to enlarge your set of solution methods.

★ Can the different approaches be grouped in any way?

Extend the activity to other calculations. Here are a few suggestions which you might like to consider:

a) 17/20 as a percentage

b) $3\frac{1}{2}^2$

c) 27×37

d) $\frac{3}{4} - \frac{2}{3}$

e) $6 \div 0.4$

f) $6 \div 2.5$

Reflections

Here are some of the methods for calculating 60% of £40 which were identified by one group of teachers:

'10% of £40 is £4, so $6 \times 4 = £24$.'

'Its got to be something to do with $6 \times 4 = 24$ and 60% is more than half — so £24.'

'$\dfrac{60}{100} \times \dfrac{40}{1} = £24$'

'0.6×40, so

$$\begin{array}{r} 40 \\ \times\ 0.6 \\ \hline £24.0 \end{array}$$

— there must be 2 figures before the decimal point.'

'60% is 3/5. 1/5 of £40 is £8, so $3 \times 8 = £24$.'

'50% is £20 and 10% is £4. That makes £24.'

The diversity of methods that these teachers used for solving this percentage problem is striking. A look at a number of textbooks will show that a wide variety of formal methods are in common use quite apart from more informal procedures.

How do pupils select a method? If you question them closely the response 'It just popped into my head' is a common explanation. Clearly the particular numbers involved may have an influence on the selection of a method. For instance, it is unlikely that you would tackle 17½% of £24 in the same way as 60% of £40.

Activities like this draw attention to the wide range of formal and more idiosyncratic methods that exist, not least among teachers, and that they exist for good reasons. We would urge you to explore the non-standard methods used by your own pupils and consider what implications this might have for your classroom practice.

Inset Activity 2:3

Here are some problems for you to try with your pupils. You may wish to devise others of your own appropriate to a particular age or ability group, but the important thing is to keep the problems easy at this stage.

1. Find the cost of 3 items at 99p each.
2. $26 + 27$
3. $1001 - 76$
4. Find: a) ¼ of 2.
   b) ¼ of 26
   c) ¼ of 29
5. What is the total length of 10 pieces of metal each measuring 2.35m?

The idea is to encourage a variety of methods of solution, so you should give some thought to how you are going to present the activity. To release children from any sense of obligation to stick to standard methods, it may be useful to use words such as:

> 'The important thing is to get the answers right — do them in any way you like.'

> 'Do them in your head if you can, but try to write down exactly how you did it.'

Issuing a piece of rough paper for the work can also help to remove inhibitions. Ask the pupils to work individually, recording both their answers and their methods of solution. Some of these will need to be clarified verbally later. Many teachers will decide to present the problems orally, but worksheet, overhead projector or blackboard may be more suitable, because this removes the time pressure on children.

Analyse the children's work carefully so that you can share and discuss your experiences with colleagues at a future meeting.

Reflections

A sensible approach to question 1 is to consider first the simpler problem of 3 items at £1. When 'nice' numbers are not evident in a problem we often seek a perspective that makes use of them.

The presentation of a problem can force students to use a standard method simply because the way it is set out is so suggestive. So,

$$26 \\ +27$$

constrains in a way that 26 + 27 does not. Writing the question 'along the line' gives the opportunity for a multiplicity of methods, often making use of easier numbers such as 20 or 25.

If question 3 is attempted in a formal way by writing it as

$$1001 \\ -76$$

it becomes rather complicated, using either decomposition or equal additions, when compared to a 'nice' number approach which, for example, sees that 1000 − 75 would give the same answer.

Question 4 illustrates the extent to which the difficulty of a problem is defined by the numbers and not simply by the operation. Whether finding a quarter is seen as 'how many 4s in . . .' or as 'halve and halve again', 24 is easier to deal with than 29.

How did you expect your pupils to do question 5? How do you feel about the outcome? For example, did they busily move the point when you would rather they either viewed it as moving the figures or worked from a rough estimate? What is the role of the 'rules of thumb' that we often use even with mental calculations of this kind? Does their successful application hinge upon an understanding of why they work?

Conclusion

The activities of this chapter have been designed to draw out the rich variety of methods that may be used to do simple calculations. Often teachers will be surprised by both the ingenuity and the underlying understanding displayed by their pupils. Although considerable emphasis is given in most schools to standard written methods and, increasingly, to the use of the calculator, most children seem able to devise effective mental methods when given suitable encouragement. Indeed they often display both greater confidence and greater ingenuity than their teachers!

In the following chapters we consider the role of written methods and calculators in relation to mental methods. Underlying our discussion is the question of the relative emphasis to be given to these three modes of calculation, an issue which is raised succinctly by Margaret Brown in the following quotation from 'Children's Understanding of Mathematics: 11 - 16', edited by Kath Hart (1981):

'It may well be the case that a combination of reliable mental methods and the ability to use a calculator are sufficient for all practical purposes. If teachers do feel it worthwhile to teach pencil and paper algorithms, then either more time must be devoted to practising and recalling them, or they must be better related to children's knowledge to assist recall. Perhaps the present methods should be abandoned in favour of others, maybe less efficient, but more related to children's own informal methods, and hence easier to remember.'

(page 47)

3 Writing It Down

```
  112              27           27        131
   23            × 19         × 19    29)3799
   49            ───          ───        29
   57            270          243        ──
 +203            243          270        89
 ────            ───          ───        87
  344            513          513        ──
   1 2            1                       29
                                         29
                                         ──
                                          —
```

'Pencil and paper represents an important and versatile resource for calculation. We believe that pupils should have effective methods of adding columns of figures, for subtraction and for multiplication (eg 27 × 6) and for division (eg 89 ÷ 4). It is of course necessary that, in using these methods, pupils **should know what they are doing . . .**'

Page 9, Mathematics for Ages 5 to 16, DES (1988)

A statement such as this raises many questions in our minds about calculations, especially the relationship between mental and written methods.

- ★ What is meant by **effective** methods?

- ★ Does the statement refer only to standard written algorithms or does pencil and paper work include pupil's own idiosyncratic methods?

- ★ Are idiosyncratic methods more or less effective than standard written algorithms?

- ★ How can we be sure that pupils 'know what they are doing'?

- ★ How can they demonstrate that they understand the methods that they use?

- ★ If children encounter differing written methods will that help them to develop a greater understanding or will it lead to increased confusion?

- ★ One of the calculations at the top of this page is incorrect. How might pupils detect and respond to errors of this kind?

- ★ Can pencil and paper methods help with developing effective mental methods?

'In their development from Key Stage 1 to Key Stage 2, pupils will make increasing use of pencil and paper methods as a versatile and convenient resource for doing calculations. These methods will, by their nature, follow the development of appropriate mental methods, which underpin all pencil and paper work.

'The term "pencil and paper methods" encompasses a wide range of formal and informal techniques and methods.'

A pupil's own recording of addition

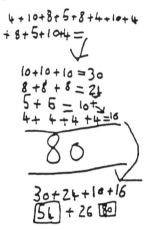

Page E3, Mathematics:
Non-Statutory Guidance
National Curriculum
Council (1989)

In considering this example of recording taken from the Non-Statutory Guidance, questions can be asked about what it reveals about the methods used by the pupil:

★   What mathematics can you see?

★   What clues are there to the thinking that the pupil is using?

★   What are the mental methods which 'underpin' the way the calculation has been done?

★   What questions might you ask to find out more about the picture the child had of the problem?

Inset Activity 3:1

> In a school of 176 children, each child is asked to bring 34 pence to pay for a performance of the puppet theatre.
>
> How much money is collected?

As a group of teachers, work out the answer to this problem in as many ways as possible, without a calculator and without using long multiplication.

Inset Activity 3:1 Continued

Discuss the methods you have used:

★ Do they match the standard algorithm using long multiplication?

★ Do they have more in common with other methods?

★ Do short cuts appear to develop?

Try a problem like this with some of your pupils, basing it on a context that is real and relevant to them. Stress that what is important is getting the correct answer, not the way in which the problem is solved. Ask them to try to write down as clearly as possible all the steps they used.

Use this material to discuss pupils' methods with your group of teachers, and consider also some questions concerning the long multiplication method.

$$
\begin{array}{r}
176 \\
\times\ 34 \\
\hline
704 \\
5280 \\
\hline
5984 \\
\hline
\end{array}
$$

★ Can pupils explain how this calculation is done using the standard method?

★ How does this compare with other methods that have been used?

★ In considering this, does the pencil and paper method reflect mental procedures?

★ What makes a method **effective?**

★ How can we encourage pupils to choose effective strategies for doing calculations?

Reflections

Using and Applying Mathematics, the new Attainment Target 1 of the National Curriculum, includes statements of attainment which say that pupils should be able to:

3(a) Find ways of overcoming difficulties when solving problems.

4(c) Give some justification for their solutions to problems.

5(a) Carry through a task by breaking it down into smaller more manageable tasks.

7(a) Follow new lines of enquiry when investigating within mathematics itself or when using mathematics to solve a real life problem.

When pupils devise and describe their own methods of doing calculations they are providing evidence of their attainment as described by statements like these. One of the difficulties with mental calculations is that the thinking remains unrecorded and the teacher often does not know how the pupil has arrived at an answer. By encouraging pupils to discuss their own methods and to write down what they have done valuable evidence of their thinking is obtained, as illustrated by this account arising out of the INSET activity.

One Person's view of 176 × 34

My first method was:

$$
\begin{array}{r}
1760 \\
1760 \\
1760 \\
176 \\
176 \\
176 \\
+176 \\
\hline
5984
\end{array}
$$

This lead me to thinking about doubling, which I find easy to do:

$$
\begin{array}{r}
352 \\
352 \\
3520 \\
+1760 \\
\hline
5984
\end{array}
$$

I then wrote down $175 = 7 \times 75$, followed by:

$$25 \times 34 = 850 \quad \rightarrow \quad 5950 \ (\times 7)$$

$$\rightarrow \quad 17850 \ (\times 3) \ \text{oops!!!}$$

My failure with this method arose through thinking that $175 = 7 \times 75$, giving an answer that did not agree with the others.

So, I changed my working to $175 = 7 \times 25$, and then did:

$$25 \times 34 = 850 \quad \rightarrow \quad 5950 \ (\times 7)$$

$$\rightarrow \quad 5984 \ (+34)$$

Having found a mistake I started to think about the methods I had been using:

★   My first method was very similar to long multiplication. I multiplied by 10 and wrote the result three times, using addition to total these with the 176 written four times.

★   The first method made me think of a short cut, which brings my method even closer to long multiplication.

★   The third method was the first time I thought of the calculation in a different way:

$$34 \times 176 = 34 \times (175 + 1)$$

$$= (34 \times 175) + (34 \times 1)$$

$$= (34 \times 25 \times 7) + (34 \times 1)$$

★   The alternative methods provide a variety of situations which can be used for checking.

★ Although I am still using mental methods, I cannot solve the problem without some writing to aid my calculation. The third method gives me a way of doing the calculation at speed, but I am still happier with the first two methods for accuracy. All three methods seem easier than my use of long multiplication:

$$
\begin{array}{r} 176 \\ \times 34 \\ \hline 5180 \\ 704 \\ \hline 5884 \end{array} \quad (???)
\qquad
\begin{array}{r} 176 \\ \times 34 \\ \hline 5280 \\ 704 \\ \hline 5984 \end{array}
$$

Where is the mistake?

Aha! Thinking about $3 \times 17 = 51$ made me forget to 'put the one on the doorstep'!

Inset Activity 3:2

$17 - x = 5$

How can this equation be solved?
Which methods are more efficient?
What do you mean by efficient?

Consider some other equations:

$$2x - 3 = 7 \qquad\qquad x^2 = 5x$$

$$x + y = 5 \quad ; \quad x - y = 3$$

Reflections

Solving the first equation mentally is very quick! $17 - 12 = 5$, therefore x is 12.

Formal solution (a):

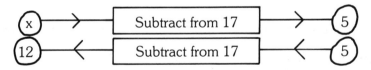

'subtract from' is self inverse

$$x = 12$$

Formal solution (b):

$$
\begin{aligned}
17 - x &= 5 \\
17 - x + x &= 5 + x && \text{Add x to both sides.} \\
17 &= 5 + x \\
17 - 5 &= 5 + x - 5 && \text{Subtract 5 from both sides.} \\
12 &= x
\end{aligned}
$$

★ How can you interpret the equation?
★ Which method is the most efficient?
★ Which have the most relevance to future work?
★ What aspects are transferable to other problems?

Inset Activity 3:3

Do written algorithms confuse thinking?

What is $\dfrac{19}{20}$ as a percentage?

Why multiply by 100?

$$\frac{19}{20} \times 100 = \frac{1900}{20}$$

Suggest alternative ways of doing the calculation.

$$= \frac{190}{2}$$

Does $\dfrac{190}{2} = 95\%$?

$$= 95\%$$

What assumptions does the written method make?

What would you do for $\dfrac{19}{30}$?

$$\frac{3\cancel{0}}{4\cancel{0}} = \frac{3}{4} \qquad \frac{3\cancel{2}}{4\cancel{2}} = \frac{3}{4}$$

Discuss.

What is it about the algorithm that can lead to such errors?

$$\frac{3\cancel{x}}{4\cancel{x}} = \frac{3}{4} \qquad \frac{3\cancel{f}}{4\cancel{f}} = \frac{3}{4}$$

What is cancelling?

What mental image does the word 'cancelling' and the crossing out create?

$$\frac{3}{4} \div \frac{2}{5} = \frac{3}{4} \times \frac{5}{2}$$

Why 'turn it upside down and multiply'?

$$= \frac{15}{8}$$

How can this be learnt with understanding?

What other methods can you use for dividing fractions?

Suggest different ways of dividing decimals. Could the same methods be used with fractions?

Inset Activity 3:4

How can we use children's responses to standard written algorithms to help with improving their understanding?

A child wrote:

$$\begin{array}{r} 2\,8 \\ +\ 3\,5 \\ \hline 5\,1\,3 \end{array}$$

What do you do about it?

$$\begin{array}{r} 5\,4 \\ -\ 2\,8 \\ \hline 3\,4 \end{array}$$

What has led to this mistake?

How should the teacher respond?

$$\begin{array}{r} 2\,4 \\ \times\ 1\,7 \\ \hline 1\,6\,8 \\ 2\,4\,0 \\ \hline 4\,0\,8 \end{array}$$

$$\begin{array}{r} 2\,4 \\ \times\ 1\,7 \\ \hline 2\,4\,0 \\ 1\,6\,8 \\ \hline 4\,0\,8 \end{array}$$

Some do it one way; some the other.

Comment and explain

Why not use a calculator?

What connection is there with
$7 \times 8 = 3 \times 8 + 4 \times 8$?

$$\begin{array}{r} 2\,7\,7\,5 \\ 2\,5\,\overline{)6\,9\,3\,7\,5} \\ 5\,0 \\ \hline 1\,9\,3 \\ 1\,7\,5 \\ \hline 1\,8\,7 \\ 1\,7\,5 \\ \hline 1\,2\,5 \\ 1\,2\,5 \\ \hline \end{array}$$

A child who can do the process wants to know why it works

Explain.

In what other ways could we write down the calculation?

Do we need to teach long division?

Is long division needed to divide algebraic expressions?

Conclusion

The place in the mathematics curriculum of standard written algorithms, particularly those relating to arithmetical calculations, remains a controversial issue. The National Curriculum is not prescriptive about methods, but it does insist that pupils should be able to carry out some calculations without a calculator.

> ★ understanding and using non-calculator methods by which a 3-digit number is multiplied by a 2-digit number and a 3-digit number is divided by a 2-digit number.
>
> Attainment target 2, level 5
> National Curriculum (1991)

Our concern in this chapter has been to raise some questions about written methods and, in particular, how their use interrelates with mental methods. It is evident that many of the standard written methods cause confusion rather than add to children's understanding. Moreover, their use outside the classroom is rapidly diminishing, as Tony Fitzgerald observes in 'New Technology and Mathematics in Employment' (1985):

> 'It has become very rare indeed to find an employee performing multiplication, division and percentage calculations, except sometimes the simpler kinds, using written methods. It is a little less rare for subtraction and addition, although for the latter a calculator will almost invariably be used if more than a handful of figures have to be totalled.'
>
> (page 38)

Mental methods are widely acknowledged to be highly useful and, by their very nature, require understanding to be used effectively. Understanding is often hindered by standard written methods and their use outside school is in rapid decline. A combination of mental and informal written methods will enable children to meet the requirements of the National Curriculum. For children to develop their powers of calculation to the full it is vital that the different methods they are encouraged to use and the ways in which they are helped to learn them are mutually compatible, appropriate to the task in hand and reinforce understanding.

4

Using Calculators

Trial and Improvement

'Mental methods have assumed a greater importance through the introduction of calculators, and the use of mental methods as a first resort in tackling calculations should be encouraged.'

Page E6, Mathematics: Non-statutory guidance
National Curriculum Council (1989)

> Find two consecutive numbers which multiply to give 1406.

Before reading on, spend a few moments with a calculator working on this problem. You may possibly be able to see an immediate way of obtaining the result, but it is more likely that you will use a simple trial and improvement procedure, and that is certainly how most children are likely to respond.

Deciding on a pair of numbers to start with is a step that children sometimes find difficult. However, whatever they start with gives useful information which helps in deciding what to try next, so there need be no fear that a guess could be wrong.

You are likely to decide fairly rapidly that you need a pair of numbers somewhere between 30 and 40, possibly from knowing that $30^2 = 900$ and $40^2 = 1600$, or perhaps by working out $30 \times 31 = 930$ and $40 \times 41 = 1640$. These calculations are likely to have been done mentally, or if they were not you will probably admit that they could have been!

Any subsequent multiplications will almost certainly need to be done with the calculator, leading quickly to the solution. One worry about using calculators is that they may just encourage blind guessing. Even working systematically through all the possibilities is not always to be commended, because, although it is safe and often produces a lot of impressive looking 'work', it may discourage thinking. We should encourage children to be on the lookout always for neater ways of solving even the simplest problems. For instance here, since 1406 ends in 6, the only two pairs worth trying are 32×33 and 37×38.

One way of giving children the encouragement to think like this and develop their mental powers is by challenging them to find such results using the **least** number of trials on their calculator. The consecutive number example can be presented as a game where one child sets a problem and challenges another to solve it with this restriction. Our first INSET activity provides another game with the same idea, which we would urge teachers to try playing themselves before introducing it in the classroom.

Inset Activity 4:1

HEX: A game for two players

Use red and yellow counters.

In turn, choose 2 numbers (or the same number twice) from the pool and multiply them.

If the answer is on the board, cover it with a counter.

The winner is the first to make a connected path between their two sides of the board.

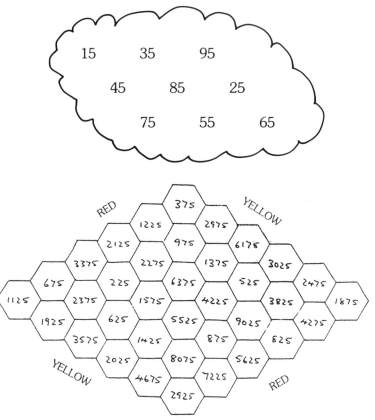

★   Play the game several times.

★   Compare the strategies you develop to help in deciding which numbers to choose.

★   Discuss how the game could be modified to suit the children you teach.

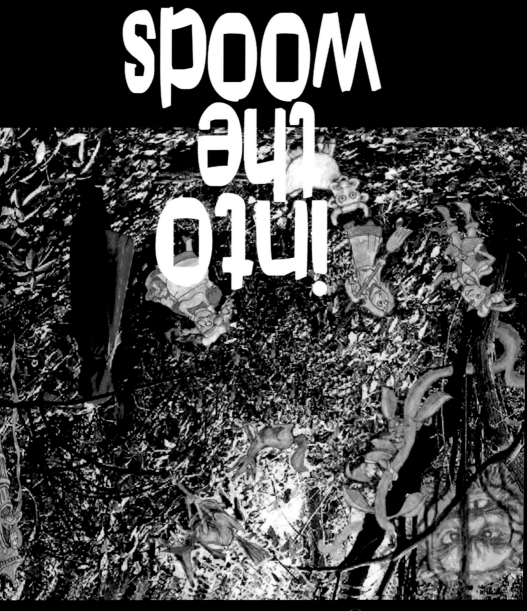

Director **KAREN HOWARD** Music Director **JAN WINSTONE** Choreographer **DAMIEN DELANEY** Design **RYAN LAIGHT**

Music & Lyrics by
STEPHEN SONDHEIM

Book by
JAMES LAPINE

into the woods

University *of* Chichester
Touring

into the woods

on tour

Thursday 15 March CHRIST'S HOSPITAL THEATRE Horsham 01403 247434
Friday 16 March HAZLITT ARTS CENTRE, EXCHANGE STUDIO Maidstone 01622 758611
Sunday 18 March GULBENKIAN THEATRE Canterbury 01227 769075
Monday 19 March REGIS CENTRE Bognor Regis 01243 861010
Tuesday 20 March THE HAWTH STUDIO Crawley 01293 553636
Thursday 22 March MEDINA THEATRE Newport, Isle of Wight 01983 527020
Saturday 24 March SALLIS BENNEY THEATRE Brighton 01273 709709
Sunday 25 March THEATRE ROYAL WINCHESTER Winchester 01962 840440

A world-wide stage sensation, Stephen Sondheim's *Into the Woods* has won multiple awards including an Olivier Award for Best Musical Revival in 2010. *Into the Woods* is witty, dark and intelligent, mashing-up the stories of fairytale characters that we have grown to love including Little Red Riding Hood, Jack and the Beanstalk, Rapunzel and Cinderella, to name but a few! The woods cast a giant shadow over them all, as they each try to make their dreams come true using great cunning and a few storylines that you definitely won't find in the original fairytales! A complex metaphor for choosing the right path, *Into the Woods* will take you on a journey in which you will discover more than just a handful of magic beans! Created by University of Chichester Touring; the same professional team that brought you last year's critically acclaimed production of *Honk!*

"The conception is brilliant. Mr. Sondheim has as much fun as one expects with his wicked airing of the old tales." New York Times on the Original Production

Recommended for 8+

Reflections

For those who are not familiar with the game of Hex it is worth playing first on a blank grid like the one at the bottom of the page. The aim is to make a connected path between the opposite sides labelled with your colour, whilst preventing your opponent connecting the other pair of sides. Appropriate strategies for this can then be developed without the added complication of thinking about the numbers.

When groups of teachers have played this game in pairs most individuals have initially found it quite difficult to make appropriate choices of numbers. After a while individuals begin to develop strategies for quickly and accurately estimating products before checking with a calculator. When a few games have been played the calculating strategies used by different individuals can be discussed, and this will usually reveal a wealth of interesting ideas.

The calculator plays a very subsidiary, but important role in the game, since the key problem is that the right pair of numbers must be selected before the calculator is used. This forces the player to do some mental calculation!

As it stands the numbers involved in the game would be too difficult for many children, but teachers will see the incentive for doing mental arithmetic that it creates. It is a simple matter to devise alternative versions of the game with simpler numbers and with other operations. Indeed children will enjoy devising their own versions. A blank Hex grid is given below to encourage you!

Inset Activity 4:1

The Story of Susan

Susan, in a year 8 class, was working on an exercise intended to be done using calculators and had just encountered the question:

What number is 777 less than 1000?

Without recourse to a calculator, Susan's immediate response was 333.

★   Discuss how the teacher might proceed.

I suggested that she should try checking her answer, which she did by working out $333 + 777 = 1110$ on her calculator. Her reaction was immediate:

'Too big. It's 110 less. 223.'

The last calculation, $333 - 110$, was done mentally without any hesitation. Although I again suggested a check, which Susan did dutifully in the same way as before, this was somewhat superfluous, for her new understanding of the situation had already made her certain that 223 was correct.

Reflections

Susan's initial response was not to think in terms of the formal subtraction $1000 - 777$, which she might have done immediately by calculator. Instead she adopted an adding on strategy which, mistakenly, seemed to her particularly simple in the case of a number whose digits were all the same. Susan had to be prompted to check her result — a quick and simple task with her calculator. A pencil and paper check might well have been so slow and cumbersome that its purpose would have been lost. In the same way calculating $333 + 777$ mentally may have been rather difficult and distracting. The use of a calculator as a checking device here was particularly valuable in furthering the mental procedure initiated by Susan.

Susan's incorrect strategy for determining 777 less than 1000 is not uncommon. The same error arises, for example, when the change from £5 for something costing £3.56 is given as £2.54.

★   Calculator checks can reveal errors which provide opportunities to increase insight and understanding.

★   Errors can act as growth points, because they may be used to provoke thought and stimulate activity.

★   The skill of the teacher lies in knowing how to capitalise on errors and use them creatively to encourage better understanding.

Inset Activity 4:3

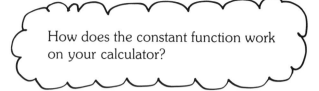

How does the constant function work on your calculator?

To add in twos try:

    [2] [+] [+] [=] [0] [=] [=] [=] . . .

       or [2] [+] [K] [=] [0] [=] [=] [=] . . .

Try it with different numbers and different operations.

Use the constant function facility to:

★   Explore multiplication patterns.

★   Investigate negative numbers.

★   Observe the effects of multiplying by 10.

★   'Hide' a constant function for a partner to identify.

Reflections

Using a constant addition function children can generate the multiples of a range of numbers very quickly. In one year 2 class this was introduced to a group. After initial free exploration, they were trying to find ways to reach a target number of 59. Counting in 2s they watched the display jump from 58 to 60. One suggested that counting in 3s would be more likely to give the missing number, but was disappointed by the result. The teacher then asked if they would like to try 4s, but one girl immediately repsonded: 'No. 4s will go straight from 56 to 60.' Exploration with the calculator had given her a very clear mental picture of the sequence of multiples.

In a year 3 class children were exploring multiples as a class activity. They used calculators to generate the sequence and recorded their results by shading in numbers on hundred squares. When they had filled in several squares they organised them into groups and tried to analyse the similarities and predict what other multiples would give similar results. The first pattern noticed was often the vertical columns of multiples of 1, 2, 5 and 10. Some children extended this to multiples of 20, and then to other multiples of multiples of 10, such as 30 and 50.

One girl, Sarah, put together a set which had no such obvious visual pattern. When asked to explain her grouping to her puzzled teacher Sarah responded: 'Can't you see? All the numbers I've shaded are even numbers and all the numbers I started with are even numbers. I think that whatever number you start with, if it is an even number, you will only get even numbers however far you go.' She went on to test this hypothesis with multiples of 72, 2658 and so on, and then to consider what happened with multiples of odd numbers. Here the calculator provided Sarah with a continuous supply of data which she could organise and analyse mentally.

In these examples the calculator supports children in exploring whatever numbers they choose. When calculators are readily available in a classroom it is very common to find young children calculating mentally with great confidence and using much larger numbers than would have been introduced in a structured mathematics scheme. The children set their own limits rather than working within limits imposed by the teacher or text.

However, calculator use does precipitate the use of small numbers too. Almost inevitably, whether by accident or design, children exploring numbers on a calculator soon discover both decimals and negative numbers. Calculator activities can then be introduced which will help them become confident in interpreting them. For example, 'hiding' a constant divisor on a calculator can encourage children to estimate with decimal numbers.

Inset Activity 4:4

Try this activity with other teachers and with children.

One player chooses a number and keys it into the calculator as a constant divisor.

Other players try to discover this number by keying in different numbers and studying the results.

For example, choose 37 and key in:

[37] [÷] [÷] [37] [=]

Now try some numbers:

	Display	Comment
[16] [=]	0.4324324	Less than half
[35] [=]	0.9459459	Close to 1, but too small.
[38] [=]	1.027027	Just too big.
[37] [=]	1	That's it! 37 ÷ 37 = 1.

Inset Activity 4:5

Find the total for each set of numbers

twice sixty five
half of one thousand
double one hundred and three

CHECK TOTAL 836

half of one thousand and two
double fifty seven
a third of ninety nine

CHECK TOTAL 648

twenty less than two hundred and forty four
ten more than two hundred and ninety three
fifty more than nine hundred and fifty three

CHECK TOTAL 1530

seven more than fifty six
three less than five hundred
thirty more than one hundred and six

CHECK TOTAL 696

★   How do you do these calculations?
    What steps do you take?
    What steps do others take?

★   What mental arithmetic is involved?

★   How do your methods vary if you write the numbers down rather than using a calculator straight away?

★   What strategies might a child who has initial difficulties with these problems develop?

★   What strategies do you have for checking?

★   Which were easy calculations to do in your head?

★   What knowledge do you bring to the situation?

Inset Activity 4:6

The Story of Wendy

Although she had produced an obviously absurd answer, Wendy, a girl in year 10, appeared not to have reacted and looked again. After all many of our older pupils have sadly ceased to believe that mathematics questions have any relation to reality, in spite of our attempts to create pseudo-real situations.

★ How would you proceed with Wendy's problem?

★ What is involved in checking whether an answer is sensible?

★ How can we encourage children to do such checks?

Reflections

The interesting thought here is that Wendy might well have found the right answer if it had not been a 'calculator' worksheet. Her chances of success would certainly have been greater if the question had been posed orally. When challenged as to whether £97.99 was a sensible answer she had no hesitation in saying it was too big, but she had no idea how she should have used the calculator and needed some prompting to think it out mentally.

There is a technical point involved here concerning how to enter prices on a calculator when some are in pounds and some are in pence, which is important in some contexts. However, the immediate problem here is best solved mentally. It is clearly important to encourage children to choose for themselves the most appropriate calculation strategy. This example emphasises the dangers of blindly using a calculator, rather than choosing a method appropriate to the problem, and draws attention to the need for children always to ask themselves: 'Is this a sensible result?'

Inset Activity 4:7

Bunny Hops

From: 'Integrating Calculators into the Primary Curriculum: Infant Pack'
Published by the Mathematical Association.

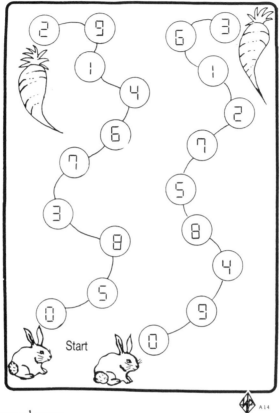

A game for two players.

By adding or subtracting numbers on your calculator, move from number to number.

The first to the carrot wins.

The same diagram (perhaps with different pictures!) can be used to play more complex games suitable for older children or adults. Multiplication and division, or operations involving negative numbers, offer a range of possibilities.

★ Devise alternative versions of the game to suit the children you teach. Try them out with a group of teachers and with children.

Talking with Six Year olds about Bunny Hops

Taking with some six year olds (year 1) about their favourite activities with the calculator, I was told about Bunny Hops and Teddy Bears Picnic (another activity from the same pack). They explained to me how to play the game by entering 'numbers and things' on the calculator and moving from one number to the next.

I asked them to explain how you played such moves as:

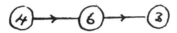

I was expecting the children to demonstrate thinking which was similar to that used in solving 'empty box' problems:

$$4 + \square = 6 \qquad\qquad 6 - \square = 3$$

All six children put 4 on the calculator display and then entered:

　　　[+] [2] [=].

For the move from 6 to 3, however, three different methods appeared:

　　　[2] [+] [1] [=], where the 2 overwrote the 6 on the display;

　　　[−] [6] [=] followed by [+] [3] [=];

　　　[−] [3] [=], which was the move I had expected.

Some of the children had not yet 'done' subtraction from their scheme, and some had as yet a very limited understanding of that process. This did not stop them from adapting their search for number operations to what they did know, namely the addition of two numbers to obtain 3 or the reduction by subtraction to 0 and then add on. The freedom to explore with a calculator enabled them to experiment.

Watching children play this game and hearing them talk about their possible moves showed how at an early age they can become excited about playing with numbers. For some young children the game has had to be adapted to include addition only, sometimes only adding one each time, but more confident children soon move on to making up their own versions of the game, often using large numbers and thus extending their mental skills and understanding.

Conclusion

When children are working with calculators opportunities for working mentally arise frequently in a variety of ways. The activities in this chapter have offered a number of contrasting situations which illustrate the interplay between calculator use and mental methods.

The calculator is a splendid tool for exploring the properties of numbers and number operations because it is both rapid and accurate. Patterns can be explored easily and trial and improvement methods can become a powerful means of solving problems. Errors can become growth points by suggesting ways forward, rather than something to be ashamed of and to be avoided.

Much opportunity for mental work arises incidentally when children are engaged in an activity. It is important to use such 'incidents' to stimulate and develop the mental powers of each child. The skill of the teacher comes in deciding when to intervene and what to say.

At the beginning of the chapter it is claimed that mental methods have taken on a 'greater importance' with the advent of calculators. Being able to do all calculations instantly on a calculator is not sufficient to ensure success in solving problems in mathematics, because the 'problem' is often to decide what numbers to use, which calculations to do and how to interpret the results. The understanding that requires can be developed through appropriate calculator activities which stimulate children to work mentally. We are greatly encouraged by the successes of the Calculator Aware Number Curriculum (CAN) reported in Calculators, Children and Mathematics (1991) where it is stated that:

> 'Many children have developed pride in not being dependent on the calculator, and prefer to use their own personal mental methods whenever possible.'

> (page 24)

5 *Speaking Out*

It might at first seem odd to devote a whole chapter to **talk** in a book about **mental** mathematics. After all, in traditional Friday morning mental arithmetic tests — as in the Key Stage 1 SATs for 1991 — even the silent movements of children's lips are regarded as a sign that they do not **know** the number facts that they are asked to record. However, throughout this book we have argued that mental mathematics involves a great deal more than simple recall of number bonds. Talking through the mental methods employed can be useful in at least two ways:

★   Talk can make public the essentially internal processes of mental mathematics, thus allowing pupils and teachers to share and extend the methods used.

★   Talk can help learners to reflect on the methods used and to focus on the important features of the problem in hand.

In some classrooms talk is a valued activity and pupils are encouraged to listen and respond to each other's ideas as they work mathematically. In other classrooms, however, mathematics is still primarily an individual activity in which pupils are not necessarily silent — they may talk to give information, instructions or answers — but they seldom use discussion to explore mathematical ideas.

In this chapter a number of activities, which involve mental methods, are described, ranging across number work, algebra, geometry and problem solving. Each one is presented within a structure designed to increase the participants' use of talk through both speaking and listening. These structures offer a useful starting point to ensure that all the participants take part and the discussion of ideas is not dominated by a vocal minority. Once speaking and listening are commonplace, participants will choose their own methods of working together and adapt the structure to suit the situation.

Teachers too may need to practise listening to other people's mathematical insights and sharing their own. Listening can be harder than talking! In order to use talk as a means of learning, the participants need to be attentive listeners. In the activities which follow the listener's role is as important as the speaker's. It is suggested that each of the activities is first used as an INSET activity with colleagues. It may then be adapted for use in any particular classroom and the outcomes discussed in future INSET meetings.

Further ideas to support mathematical discussion can be found in Maths Talk, published by Stanley Thornes for the Mathematical Association (1987).

Inset Activity 5:1

Follow My Leader

All these activities are for two people A and B, working together. A large cardboard box on its side can act as a useful hide for one person's work.

1. A makes a design using coloured plastic shapes or interlocking cubes.

    A then **instructs** B how to make the same design.

    B's final result is compared with A's prototype.

2. As above, but this time A **covers** the original design before instructing B how to make it.

    In this way A has to rely on a mental image of the shape.

3. A describes a route round the neighbourhood or school.

    B says where the route described would lead.

    Results may need to be compared on a map!

    In this case both A and B work with a mental image throughout.

★   Are there any differences between A's intentions and B's results?

★   Do we use different strategies when using mental images, as in 2 and 3 above, rather than when using objects, as in 1?

Inset Activity 5:2

Try these activities with a group of teachers and then in the classroom. Discuss the outcomes at a subsequent INSET meeting.

1.   Target Ten

One person leads the group by slowly reciting a series of instructions describing operations on numbers.

Start with 6   Add 3   Take 2   Add 5

Take 4   Add 2   . . . . .

Everybody else tries to keep a running total mentally and shouts '10' when this number is reached. The first person to do so correctly takes over the role of leader.

2.   Home Again

Each person thinks of a number less than ten and manipulates it according to the instructions of the leader, shouting 'home' when she or he returns to the number first thought of.

For example 'add 1, multiply by 2, subtract 2, halve' is 'home' for all, but 'multiply by 2, add 1 subtract 2' is 'home' for 1 only.

★   Can the group work out the starting number each time?

3.   Playing 'Out'

This is like Home Again, but with no single leader. Players take turns to give one instruction with the aim of getting other players 'home' while remaining 'out' themselves.

In the examples given so far we have stressed the role of the listener in becoming involved in the mathematics. The next activity offers a strategy which can help to give everyone an opportunity to **talk,** as well as to listen.

There is always a tension in using whole class discussion in the classroom. If the teacher acts as chair, then often only a few will speak and even these speakers may rely on the teacher to endorse statements made. There is then little incentive to listen carefully. On the other hand, if the teacher organises discussion in smaller groups, more people will speak, but the teacher and the class are not able to listen to everything that is said. The exercise which follows offers one way of organising discussion so that all the participants speak and every idea is worked on.

Inset Activity 5:3

Sum Talk

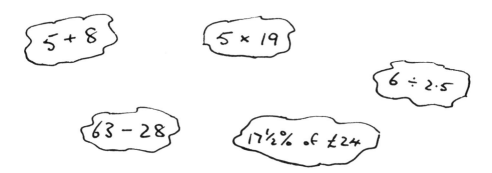

Pose any appropriate mathematical question to the class and allow time for everyone to solve it mentally.

In pairs

Ask participants to agree the answer and exchange methods.

Allow time for them to discuss how similar, and how different, their methods are.

In fours made up of two pairs

Each person describes her or his partner's method.

The partner may refine the description if necessary.

Again the whole group should consider carefully all the methods and decide how many distinct approaches there really are.

In eights made up of two fours

At this point it is probably necessary for each group to appoint one speaker from each four to report to the whole group, concentrating on the comparison of methods.

Finally, as a whole class

Each group of eight reports back.

Reflections

A class of year 2 children went through the Sum Talk activity to discuss the simple problem of adding 5 and 8. Their recent mathematical experience included using a variety of apparatus to model number with each child working from a separate card selected by the teacher. They were not used to talking about **how** they did their work, although they would readily swap ideas or advice. Although this was a new task, they willingly began to share their methods of working. They were intrigued to find that a sum, which has only one correct answer, could be done in so many ways. No two accounts were identical but the children readily began to sort themselves into those who had 'seen things' in their minds and counted them up; those who had used their fingers or other parts of the body and 'felt' the numbers and the few (there were only three) who just 'knew something'.

Alex	I made the five into a one and a four because I know 9 and 4 is 13.
Sarah	I said: '8 and 5, 9 and 4, 10 and 3, 11 and 2, 12 and 1 — it's 13!'
Katharine	I saw it written in a book, and the answer just wrote itself in!

A teacher listening in to their discussions might make further distinctions and use them to inform future work with the children. For instance those who 'saw things' included children who 'saw' five objects and eight objects separately and then combined them and those who 'saw' five **or** eight objects and used them to count on from the other number — two very different strategies.

In 1991, the Key Stage 1 SAT for Attainment Target 3 included a similar activity in which children had to add two numbers on specially prepared dice. The teacher had to assess whether they did this through recall or through any other means. This was judged usually by the speed of response from the child. In the class above, only Katharine **knew** the relevant number bond. Alex and Sarah used other mathematical strategies to access the number bonds they did know. The other children all used counting strategies. Some of them were, however, very quick at it and, unless they had described the method used, the teacher would not have known that Katharine's method was unique. Repeating the SAT assessment activity with a group of teachers who taught mathematics from primary to university level, a similar range of strategies was described. Only two of the eight people consistently 'knew' the required number facts, the rest used a variety of strategies like Sarah and Alex. There were, however, very few instances of **counting** as a method!

Such simple examples as these can help to demonstrate which addition bonds children do recall. More complex examples give children the opportunity to share the strategies they use when recalled facts are not enough. The following examples demonstrate some of the strategies used for subtraction by children of the same age following the Calculator Aware Number Curriculum (CAN). Many further examples in the same vein will be found in the book 'Calculators, Children and Mathematics' (1991) by Hilary Shuard and others, which describes the CAN Curriculum in detail.

Subtract 28 from 63

'I added on 30 to get 58, then another 2 to make 60 and then 3 more, that makes 35 altogether.'

'I took 30 away to give 33, then added 2 back.'

'20 from 60 is 40. 8 from 3 is negative 5. The answer is 35.'

'Two 30s are 60 and you need to add at both ends, so you get 35.'

In all these examples, by asking the group to **describe** the methods they used to reach a solution, they make public the internal processes of the mental mathematics they have used. This can inform the teacher's assessment of their understanding of number and, through inviting the groups to **compare** their methods of solution, they are encouraged to reflect on the processes used and to extend their own repertoire of strategies.

Discussing Mathematics

The first three activities have suggested ways in which simple activities can be structured to increase the involvement of every member of the group in speaking and listening. The actual tasks can be altered to suit any group of teachers or any particular classroom. You may also want to consider ways of encouraging your pupils to share ideas about the mathematics they are using without the need to structure the discussion. One way of increasing the incentive to discuss mathematics is to present the work differently. An exercise from a book or workcard only needs to be completed, not discussed. If the content of an exercise is presented as a game or an investigation, then there is more reason to share the methods used because doing so can help to carry the game or investigation forward. In this situation pupils not only **say** what they are doing, but are more likely to express their ideas about **why** a method works and to **try out** the methods used by others.

Here are two examples from children in year 5 whose attainment in mathematics (as assessed by standardised tests) was very low. An exercise on computation written in a book or on a test paper would cause consternation among the group. Even trying to say or show how they arrived at a particular answer was usually a daunting task for them. However, the following two transcripts from their work on games show that, within this context, they were able to demonstrate and explain a variety of competent strategies for accurate mental calculation and were able to offer each other help and advice.

1.   The group was playing a simple game of Snakes and Ladders in which each player had to complete a calculation before climbing a ladder:

Victoria	You've got 17 + 56.
Hayley	Oh, that's 56 + 17.
Victoria	No, 17 + 56.
Hayley	Well, it's all the same and anyway mine's easier! 57, 58, 59, 60, . . . **73!**
Karl	Mine's 27 + 38. 20 and 30 is 50. Fifty eight. 59, 60, 61, 62, 63, 64, **65!**

---

2.   A second game involved a variation of 'Snap', but the aim was to collect cards which totalled 10. Until this point in the game, only pairs of cards had been taken.

Hayley	I can do this: 2 and 2 and 6.

Later Hayley took 5 and 3 and 2. This included one of Victoria's cards.

Victoria	That's not fair. You've changed the rules when I was looking for a five.
Nozmul	It is fair. 3 and 2 **is** 5.
Victoria	But before 5 and 5 made 10. Now lots of things make 10!

Despite this complaint, Victoria readily adapted to the new rule.

Inset Activity 5:4

Taped Talk

As an INSET group, try adapting an exercise to make a game and comparing the sort of discussion that is generated by each type of activity.

First you need to find an appropriate exercise perhaps taken from your usual maths scheme. Then devise a simple game which involves some similar calculations. The Snakes and Ladders game described above is a very easy one to adapt. Then tape record the talk of groups of children: some completing the exercise and some playing the game. Discuss these recordings at an INSET meeting.

★ What do the groups talk about?
   How much of the talk is about the activity?
   How much of it is about how they are actually doing the calculations?

★ Listen again to any of the talk that **is** about the way they do the calculations. What does it tell you about the speaker's mental methods?

★ Is there any difference in the usefulness of the talk generated by the two activities?

★ As a group, can you devise further activities which might increase the amount of talking about methods and strategies used?

★ Try them out in class!

In problem solving we sometimes have an intuition or feel for what is happening, but, unless we can put it into words, it is difficult to be sure if it is useful. Talking about it offers the opportunity to test and refine one's intuition.

One way to encourage productive talk is to have groups of pupils working together when solving problems. However, an activity which begins through cooperative group work can easily become one in which a group is sitting together with each person busily pursuing an individual line of thought, putting ideas on paper, but not being willing to slow down and share them. In this situation it is often only when someone has become stuck that she or he will readily seek to share ideas. At this point the teacher, or other listener, is cast in the role of one who is expected to offer a way out of the immediate problem, rather than someone who will appreciate the success of what has already been achieved. It can be very difficult to recreate the powerful thinking that went into a partial solution rather than just to articulate the immediate problem.

With the suggestions for the next INSET activity this difficulty is partially avoided by using the people in the group to model the problem themselves. It would be easy to recast these situations into ones using counters or symbols, but to do so too soon might limit the opportunities for using talk to share insights. Try each activity first with other teachers and later with pupils. If you have considered these problems before in another setting, think how using people as players modifies the way you proceed towards a solution.

Inset Activity 5:5

Don't Push Me Around!

1. For a group of 4

   A fast and furious river is flowing through the classroom and you need to cross it to get to the door. You represent a family of four: two adults and two children. Each of you can row but the little boat you have will only hold one adult or two children at any one time. How can you safely reach the other side by boat?

2. For a group of 8

   Stand yourselves in the cells of an imaginary 3 by 3 square leaving one corner square empty. The person in the diagonally opposite corner has to move into that position but players can only move one square at a time forwards, backwards or sideways into an empty square. Try solving the problem several times.

   ★   Can you do it silently?

   ★   Can you do it in fewer moves?

   ★   How would you organise the moves for a bigger square?

3. For a group of 3

   Put three chairs in a row. Each person can either stand up or sit down. A **move** is for two people to change their positions from sitting to standing or vice versa. Start with all three standing up. By using moves as described, can you get all three sitting down at the same time?

   ★   Change the number of players or the number of people involved in a move and explore the situation further.

Mathematics is often thought of as a difficult subject to teach because of the large number of abstract ideas it uses from the very beginning. Of course we know when we have introduced a group to squares, square roots or secants, but do we know what they really think they are? Using talk can help them to clarify their own minds and refine their own ideas. It can also help us as teachers to gain far greater understanding of the conceptions and misconceptions pupils have, and to act appropriately. Pupils' naive theories can be very enduring if they remain unchallenged — as one helpful child explained to a researcher: 'a rectangle is about twice the size of a square'! (p.32, 'Children Learning Mathematics' by Dickson, Brown and Gibson)

The final INSET activity in this chapter invites you to uncover what your own pupils make of the mathematical terms they use. One or more members of your INSET group could organise and record a class discussion to use with the group. If it is difficult to tape your own pupils, you might like to consider the three discussions about triangles which follow — they are not untypical!

Inset Activity 5:6

What is it?

What is a diagonal? A decimal? A derivative?

Consider any concept recently introduced, or used, in your classroom.

Organise and record a discussion between groups of pupils in which they decide what . . . is and consider examples and counter examples. You might ask them to prepare an explanation for a visitor who does not know the term.

Listen to the tape in your INSET group and note down the mental images used in explaining the concept in question.

★ Are there any surprises?

★ What are the implications for teaching topics which use this concept?

★ What are the implications for teaching other topics?

Talking Triangles

The following classroom discussions illustrate some of the difficulties young children face even with such an apparently simple concept as 'triangle'.

1.   A reception class was prepared to draw cats. The children began by looking at one their teacher had already drawn. Through question and answer they identified the head as a 'circle', the body as an 'oval', the ears as 'triangles' and the whiskers as 'lines'. They agreed to do the same on their own drawings, and set to work. However, though the bodies, heads and whiskers came out as recognisable shapes, the ears were extraordinarily varied! Some were looped and twisted; some were single lines; some had many sides; some were possibly triangular. Nonetheless, when asked about their drawings, the children all agreed that **all** the ears and **only** the ears were 'triangles'. They were certain about this because, as they explained, 'teacher told us'! Teacher, of course, had done no such thing, but how were these children to know that there is a fundamental difference in how you use the words 'ear' and 'triangle'? All the children had drawn 'ears'. Any pair of marks attached to the 'head' would have been a pair of 'ears', but only some of these marks of a particular shape are 'triangles'.

2.   A Year 2 class helpfully offered to instruct a visitor how to draw a triangle. They readily suggested a diversity of images:

> 'It's a mountain'.
>
> 'A pyramid'.
>
> 'The roof of a house'.
>
> 'The point of a pencil'.
>
> 'A cone without an ice cream'.
>
> 'It's a shape'.
>
> 'It's got a point at the top'.
>
> 'It's got three corners and a line at the bottom'.
>
> 'It's like a four with another line and a little bit rubbed out'.
>
> 'It's bigger — about an inch long'.

However, they were not satisfied with the artistic interpretations of their descriptions until an equilateral triangle with its base parallel to the bottom edge and about an inch long was drawn.

3. A group of children from Year 3 and Year 4 became caught up in an unplanned discussion trying to distinguish between triangles and right angles:

Teacher	Is this (△) a triangle?
Class	Yes.
Teacher	Is this (◿) a triangle?
Class	No!
Teacher	Why is this (△) a triangle but this (◿) not?
Luke	That's (△) a triangle, and that's (◿) a right angle.
Simon	It's not a right angle.
Luke	What is it then?
Simon	It's a triangle.
Luke	No it's not, **that's** (△) a triangle.
Simon	It's not a right angle because a right angle isn't a shape.
Teresa	A right angle is ninety degrees.
Laura	What's 'degrees'?
Laura	A triangle has to have two equal sides but it could have more.
Teacher	Is this (◿) a triangle then?
Laura	Yes.
Teacher	Why?
Laura	Because it just **is**.
Teresa	I think it might be a right angle, but I think it could be a triangle . . . ?
Simon	It's not a right angle. It's a triangle.
Teresa	How do you know?
Luke	It's not a triangle anyway.
Teacher	Why don't you think it's a triangle?
Luke	Because all the triangles I've ever seen in books look like that (△).
Teacher	So you've never seen a triangle any other way?
Luke	Well, I haven't read all that many books on triangles, but all the ones I have seen are like that.
Teacher	If you think this (◿) is a triangle, explain why.
Laura	A triangle has three lines.
Sam	And three corners.
Teresa	If you fold a circle in half and half again you get three sides and three corners, but it's not a triangle.
Simon	The sides have to be straight lines.
Teacher	So you think a triangle is any shape with three straight sides and three corners?
Class	Yes.
Luke	No, I still don't think so. Not **any** shape.

6 *Pictures in Your Mind*

Pentominoes

In this chapter we consider some ways in which children can be encouraged to use mental imagery as a strategy in tackling problems, by envisaging and then transforming mathematical pictures.

To illustrate this, the problem of deciding whether a pair of shapes are congruent provides a simple example. Look at the two pentominoes below and consider how you go about deciding whether they are the same.

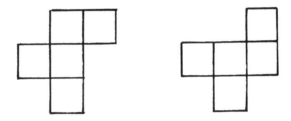

How do you approach this? Do you draw the shapes and cut them out? It is more likely that you took one of the shapes and transformed it mentally in some way until it fitted neatly on top of the other. For example, you may have mentally rotated the left hand shape by a quarter turn anti-clockwise, as shown below, and then realised that it was the mirror image of the other shape.

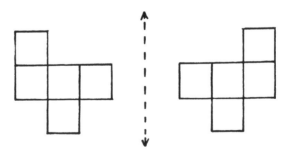

The ability to handle mental images in this way is a powerful facility and one that we might usefully seek to cultivate more in children. The INSET activities in this chapter provide some opportunities for you to explore possible strategies for developing such mental imagery. As with activities in other chapters they can be both explored by a group of teachers working together, and also tried with children, providing material for comparison and discussion at a subsequent INSET gathering.

Inset Activity 6:1

1. Look at a cube built from eight smaller cubes. How many more blocks would have to be added to make the next sized cube?

Describe carefully the methods used to find the solution.

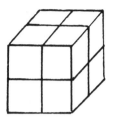

2. Place two right angled isosceles triangles on an overhead projector, or on the table, if you are working with a small group.

What different shapes can be made by placing the triangles together so that a pair of edges coincide?

Take plenty of time to visualise the different shapes that you can make. Describe how to move the triangles to make each shape.

---

3. Make part of a square pattern as shown, using alternate red and blue counters.

What will be the colour of the peg in the lower right hand corner of the square?

What will be the colour of the one above it?

R	B	R	B
B	R	B	
R	B		
B			

Will there be more red pegs or blue pegs in the completed pattern?

What happens if a five by five square is created?

What about larger squares?

Reflections

Here are three responses to the cube problem:

'I put four more cubes on each of the three faces. Then, two in the gaps on each of the edges and one in the hole in the corner! That's 12 and 6 and 1: 19 altogether.'

'It's got to be 27 in the bigger cube. $27 - 8 = 19$.'

'There's 4 on the top, 6 on the side and 9 on the front. That makes 19.'

To understand the first and last explanations is an additional test of the reader's powers of mental imagery, whereas the second neatly avoids visualisation by using familiarity with the cubes of 2 and 3.

This activity can easily be simplified by working in two dimensions with squares and other shapes, or extended by thinking of larger cubes, or cuboids. In an algebraic context there are links with the identity:

$$(x + 1)^3 = x^3 + 3x^2 + 3x + 1$$

A wide range of discussion can be stimulated by the two triangles problem, because many children will feel that there are far more than **three** distinct shapes. For instance, the pairs shown below will often be seen as two different shapes.

The activity can be easily modified by using three or more triangles, or different shapes.

It is interesting again to compare the way in which different individuals see the counters pattern. Here are three people's ways of deciding the colour in the lower right hand corner:

'I counted B R B R on my fingers.'

'It's the same as the second row. Ends in red'.

'It goes red all down the middle!'

In each of these problems an image has been provided which can be manipulated mentally. The problems can, of course, be tackled using concrete materials and we make no suggestion here that this should not normally be encouraged, because children need a rich experience of concrete images to draw upon. However in this chapter our interest is particularly focussed upon mental imagery, so some restrictions are imposed.

Inevitably some children (and also some teachers!) find visualisation, particularly of 3 dimensional objects, easier than others. The challenge for the teacher is to try to improve and extend all children's visualisation skills.

A variety of both practical materials and pictorial representations are introduced to children in school to model numerical concepts, and yet we know very little about how children's mental images relate to these imposed models. The same is also true of pictures and materials used in a geometrical context. Does the child 'see' the same thing as the teacher or the designer of the classroom material? This draws attention to the value of encouraging talk about the mental images that a particular problem provokes. As with mental arithmetic, talk is of value to both the speaker who has to reflect on the methods used and to the listeners who are able to share in and learn from the images and ideas.

The next two activities involve problems with a cube. We suggest using them without a picture or concrete model, so that no particular image is imposed on the individual, and different mental images can be explored.

Inset Activity 6:2

Painting a Cube

Visualise a solid 4 by 4 by 4 cube.

★   How many faces?

★   How many vertices?

★   How many edges?

Imagine that the whole surface of the cube is painted and that it is then cut into unit cubes.

★   How many unit cubes?

★   How many of these cubes have paint on no faces?

★   How many are painted on just one face?

★   How many are painted on 2, 3, 4. . . . faces?

Inset Activity 6:3

Cutting a Cube

Visualise a solid 3 by 3 by 3 cube.

The problem is to make a series of plane cuts in order to obtain 27 unit cubes.

The pieces can be reassembled in any way after each cut.

What is the minimum number of cuts required?

Prove it!

This problem can be a very fruitful source of discussion. Teachers in an INSET group and children in the classroom should be encouraged to explore their mental images by being asked to describe what they 'see' and how they are thinking about the problem. Here are some questions that you may find it useful to pursue.

★ What images of the cube are conjured up by different people?

★ How do you 'see' different views of the cube in your mind?

★ How do you visualise the cuts taking place?

★ To what extent can you move the pieces around and reassemble them?

★ What makes you certain that you are making sufficient cuts to release all the cubes?

★ Can you do it with less cuts?

★ How can you be sure that you have found the minimum number of cuts? Can you prove it?

★ Describe the 'Eureka' moment when the insight came to you about the minimum number or when you grasped somebody else's explanation.

Visualising Numbers

Geometrical images can provide a powerful way of looking at numbers and their properties. The number line is a geometrical representation and number squares use the position of numbers to draw attention to particular properties. Diagrams are commonly used to illustrate odd and even numbers or fractions, and the area of a rectangle is a common model for multiplication. Many words used in a number context draw attention to these geometrical links and encourage us to picture the numbers. Squares, cubes and triangle numbers are all very familiar.

The familiar 'staircase' diagram for a triangle number can be used neatly to arrive at a general way of calculating the value of any triangle number.

The diagram helps to show why the fourth triangle number is a half of 4×5, leading to the general formula $\frac{1}{2}n(n + 1)$.

Inset Activity 6:4

Each of these examples can be explored numerically or algebraically, but the intention here is to explore them mentally as 'pictures in your mind'.

Explain what happens if you:

★   Add two even numbers.

★   Add two odd numbers.

★   Add an odd number and an even number.

★   Add two consecutive triangle numbers.

★   Subtract two consecutive triangle numbers.

★   Add three consecutive numbers.

★   Add three consecutive odd (or even) numbers.

★   Add a number to its square.

★   Subtract a number from its square.

★   Subtract one from a square number.

Reflections

A diagram can help you to 'see' very neatly why adding two odd numbers always gives an even number.

Looking at the sum of a few sets of three consecutive numbers soon makes you think that the result is always a multiple of three.

$$3 + 4 + 5 = 12$$
$$8 + 9 + 10 = 27$$
$$14 + 15 + 16 = 45$$
$$29 + 30 + 31 = 90$$

Further investigation leads to the fact that it is three times the middle number always. Why this should be so is again clarified by a picture, which may indeed suggest the result in the first place.

One less than a square number is easy to picture as a unit square cut from the corner of a bigger square. A slice off the top placed at the side produces a rectangle, which someone said was 'one less by one more', which is a good way of describing the formal relationship $n^2 - 1 = (n - 1)(n + 1)$.

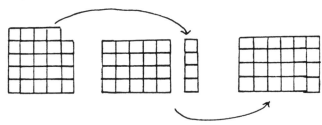

Conclusion

In conclusion let us remember that our starting point was using mental imagery as a possible strategy for tackling problems. We have suggested in this chapter a number of ways in which the use of mental pictures of all kinds can be explored and maybe developed.

This must remain a very speculative area, for we know very little about how, and indeed whether, people's ability to visualise geometrical objects can be developed. Many people, including many professional mathematicians, say that they find it very difficult to form useful mental pictures of geometric objects. Others observe that they frequently think in terms of pictures in the mind and find this a valuable source of insight. At least we can provide all children with some opportunities to explore their mental powers in this area.

7

Micros and Mental Methods

In this chapter we look at a number of items of computer software in order to highlight ways in which opportunities for doing mental mathematics can arise. A wide range of software is available for use in the classroom and we make no attempt to offer a comprehensive view, but rather to share some examples related to the theme of this book. Further details, including suppliers of the programs mentioned, appear at the end of the chapter.

A great deal has been written about the use of LOGO in schools and many different benefits are claimed for it. Turtle geometry is the best known application of LOGO. Here we see the screen turtle, indicated by an arrow, which pupils have been moving to draw a house on the screen. They have started at the top left corner of the rectangle and used just the two commands forward (fd) and right (rt).

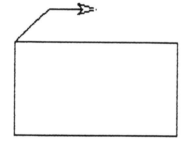

```
rt  90
fd  250
rt  90
fd  150
rt  90
fd  250
rt  90
fd  150
rt  45
fd  50
fd  25
rt  45
fd  50
```

★ Follow through the commands above to see how the house has been drawn so far.

★ What might the next command be?

★ How do you judge the length of the rooftop?

★ What happens if you use trial and error?

★ What angle will you need to turn through to complete the roof?

★ What happens if the roof is pitched at a different angle?

When drawing their house some children automatically pitch their roof at 45 degrees and confidently turn right 45 degrees at the other end. Others argue about the pitch of the roof and then have to consider carefully the angle of turn at the other end. Another approach is to attempt to draw the angle by eye until it is realised that there is a connection between the angles. Difficulties inevitably arise in making the roof meet the wall at the other end.

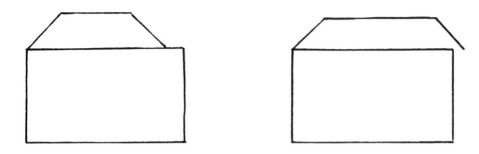

Pupils sometimes extend the house to fit the roof and the extra line '. . . is the drainpipe'! Perhaps a simpler strategy would be to draw the roof first!

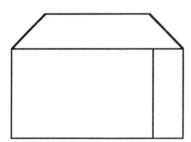

Working with LOGO places children in an environment where they are encouraged to form mental images as they look for solutions to the problems that arise. They are constantly aided by feedback from the screen as their ideas develop. There is a strong stimulus in our example to create a house that looks 'right', and this involves important ideas of length, angle and proportion.

Many teachers will have noticed the excitement and enthusiastic activity which takes place when children are using a computer. We hope that the activities which follow will offer some ideas about how working with computers can be used to stimulate and enhance the mental skills of all kinds which we feel are vital to children's full mathematical development.

Inset Activity 7:1

PREDICT, FACTOR	MicroSMILE: the first 31
TRAINS, TARGET	Number Games, Anita Straker
ERGO	SLIMWAM 1, ATM
MONTY	SLIMWAM 2, ATM

Choose a program, such as one of those listed above, which involves working with numbers.

Work through the program in groups of two or three, perhaps look at a second program and then discuss your thoughts with other groups.

Here are some questions you might like to consider:

Is the program interesting?
★   Would it hold children's attention?
★   Would they want to use it more than once?

What mental mathematics is involved?
★   Did you have a strategy?
★   Do children need a strategy?
★   What mental imagery does it provoke for you?
★   Did you use any model that you already had?
★   What might you expect children to do?

What mental arithmetic could be used?
★   What knowledge do you need?
★   What calculations do you have to do?
★   How did you do them?
★   Is there anything which may cause anxiety?
★   Is this likely to affect children's thinking?
★   Would a calculator aid or impede the activity?

Is it sociable?
★   Is more than one person involved?
★   What did you discuss?
★   What might children gain from discussion?

If the program provoked discussion, try it with some children when you are in a position to overhear what is going on. If it is possible to tape their discussion, this would provide very useful material for a subsequent INSET session.

Inset Activity 7:2

Using COUNTER: a program that just counts!

[SLIMWAM 2, ATM]

There are many ways of using this program with children of all ages from infants to sixth form. Explore some possibilities with your INSET group and note particularly the opportunities that arise for mental mathematics.

Using one counter:

★   What comes next?

★   Can you count up in twos?

★   Can you count up in fours?

★   What about 1, 7, 13, . . .?

★   Can you get negative numbers?

★   Can you get decimal numbers?

★   Can you get triangle numbers?

★   What happens if you count up in tenths?

★   What happens if you listen to the units when you are counting in twos, or threes . . .?

Using two counters:

★   One counter is set so that its number is one more than the number on the other counter. One counter is then hidden. Can you stop the counters when the hidden number is 10, 15, . . .?

★   One counter shows   3   6   9   12   15 . . .
    and the other   5   10   15   20   25 . . .

    Hide one counter. Can you stop the count when the hidden counter shows 30?

★   How can you set the counters up, one counting in threes and the other in fives so that you can stop them with both at the same number?

★   If the starting number on one counter is 25 and on the other 13, how can you get both counters to arrive at the same number after six moves?

    . . . or after three moves, twelve moves, twenty four moves?

Try out an activity using COUNTER with some children and discuss their responses and the strategies they used with your INSET group.

Two Accounts of Working with Counter

Working with some year 1 children, I was using two counters set up so that one was always one more than the other. We looked at the counters as they changed, with the children predicting what pairs of numbers would appear next.

Counter 1:	0	1	2	3	4	5	6	7	8	9
Counter 2:	1	2	3	4	5	6	7	8	9	10

I then hid the lower number. The children were asked about the relationship between the visible and hidden numbers. 'Add 1' and '1 more' were the common responses. The counters were then set off from the beginning again. I asked the children to tell me to stop the counters when the hidden number was 5 or 7 or whatever they chose. After a few false starts, they found this easy, even for numbers in the thirties and forties.

However when the upper number was hidden it appeared to be much more difficult, even though ideas such as '1 off' or '1 less' were discussed before we started. Eventually the children began to plan ahead before the counters were set off. They still got distracted and needed to make both counters visible to check their ideas, but they were willing to make several attempts at the same target number.

A group of year 10 students were using two counters with starting numbers of 25 and 13. They had to choose the step size to make both counters reach the same number after **six** steps. First attempts were by trial and error as in this example.

25	26	27	28	29	30	31
13	15	17	19	21	23	25

Eventually they found a successful route.

25	26	27	28	29	30	31
13	16	19	22	25	28	31

The challenge then was to find other solutions. The largest number which could be found was soon being discussed. Finding the smallest number caused interesting arguments:

'It can only end at 25.'   'No, 13.'
'I've got to 1.'   'I can get lower, I've got to -11'.

This was the first stage at which the pupils reached for pencil and paper. Calculations had been done in their heads up to that point, but now different ideas had to be tested and they needed to record in order to be able to remember what they had already tried. Their explanations of what was happening led on to linear graphs and notions of gradient. They had met such topics before, but for the first time they were choosing these ideas for themselves to explain what was happening, rather than being told to use them by the teacher.

Inset Activity 7:3

Looking at TAKEHALF: how to halve a square!

[from MicroSMILE: the first 31]

This program from SMILE operates like a film, generating pictures of a square being continuously divided in half in different ways. Half the picture is black and half is white as the animation moves and divides, producing squares, triangles and many other shapes. The picture can be frozen at any time by simply pressing the space bar.

 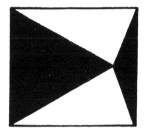

In your INSET group, try the following:

Stop the picture. Ask yourselves questions such as:

★   What shapes can be seen?
★   How can they be described?
★   Are any shapes the same?
★   Is it half black?
★   Can you prove it?

Stop the picture. Allow yourselves a short time to look at it and then switch off the monitor.

★   What can you remember or reconstruct?
★   How do you describe what you can remember?
★   Can this program help to develop visual memory?
★   Does it encourage you to create and transform pictures in your mind?
★   How can talk about the images be encouraged?
★   What ideas about symmetry are involved?
★   What thoughts about area does it stimulate?
★   What sort of 'hands off' activities could be used to enhance work based on TAKEHALF in the classroom.

Inset Activity 7:4

SOLVE ME: $23x - 19 = 52$

An activity using either LOGO or BASIC.

Enter this procedure using LOGO.	Enter this short program using BASIC.
TO TRY 'X PRINT 23 ★ :X − 19 Type TRY 2, TRY 3 and so on until you find a value that gives an output of 52.	10 INPUT X 20 PRINT 23★X − 19 30 GOTO 10 RUN this program. At the prompt enter 2, then 3 and so on until you find a value that gives an output of 52.

★ Which numbers did you try?
★ Was the process you used 'trial and error' or was it 'trial and improve'?
★ How quickly did you get a solution?
★ What knowledge about numbers did you bring to the process of solution?
★ Do the easily generated 'answers' deter you from looking for short cuts?
★ How does this process provide a different insight into the solution of equations?

You may like to try out this activity with a variety of alternative equations:

$$3x + 5 = 15 \qquad 11x + 7 = 19$$

$$16x - 2 = 59 \qquad 8x + 12 = 7$$

$$20 - 3x = 12 \qquad 13 - 25x = 4$$

$$x^2 = 289 \qquad x^2 = 10$$

$$x^2 + x = 3 \qquad x(x + 1) = 5$$

$$x^2 - 3x - 5 = 0 \qquad x^3 - x = 12$$

$$1/x = 0.8 \qquad 1/x = 8$$

Reflections

A group of adults, working on different aspects of solving equations, was given the LOGO procedure to solve $23x - 19 = 52$ in order to illustrate the process of using trial and improvement, and to demonstrate another aspect of LOGO.

A number of them were fascinated by being able to type 'TRY 2' which resulted in a response of 27. Part of their fascination was actually because of the label 'TRY', which had been attached to the procedure so that the language was natural to them. The rest was the fascination of answers appearing at speed. They became very involved in trying to home in on the value of x which produced 52. They seemed to enjoy finding the difference between 52 and the result at each stage. For some it was a good ten minutes before they attempted to solve the equation by more formal methods, which, as secondary teachers, were very familiar to them.

In the discussion which followed many of them felt that they were improving their 'feel' for number by using this method. Although they were used to solving linear equations, this particular method was unfamiliar to some, and they were intrigued at finding an alternative way of obtaining an answer. They argued that it helped them to understand the equation in a different way.

Working with a micro in this way led them along a particular track which prevented other more familiar approaches being considered. The novelty of the approach and the inherent satisfactions of the 'homing in' process seem to have prevented them from seeing the relevance of their existing knowledge. However, the process encourages new insights about number and equations and provides a simple, but powerful, means of solving equations of all kinds.

As an alternative to the programs above the technique of trial and improvement can be used in conjunction with a spreadsheet. By means of a template which uses an increment the search for solutions can be displayed in a systematic way, and the ordering of the numbers helps to highlight the position of the solution.

x	$23 \star x - 19$	
1	4	increment 1
2	27	
3	50	
4	73	
5	96	

x	$23 \star x - 19$	
3	50	increment 0.1
3.1	52.3	
3.2	54.6	
3.3	56.9	
3.4	59.2	

Inset Activity 7:5

Using SPREADSHEETS

Numerical data can be set up in advance on a spreadsheet and can provide opportunities for predicting and hypothesising about the effect of making changes to the data.

Try this example in your INSET group:

	01	02	03	04
01		Cost (p)	Number	Total
02	Beans (tin)	45	2	90
03	Bread (loaf)	60	1	60
04	Butter (0.25kg)	75	1	75
05	Cheese (0.25kg)	70	1	70
06				
07				2.95

Columns 2 and 3 contain data and column 4 is the product of the numbers in column 2 and column 3.

If only the data in column 3 is allowed to be changed:
★ Can you spend exactly £6?
★ Can you spend exactly £7, £8, £5, £10?
★ What amounts can you spend?
★ If you can change the prices as well, what happens?
★ How did you tackle the problem?
★ What mental mathematics did you use?

Reflections

A group of year 7 children working on this problem talked a lot about the mental calculations they were doing as they looked for solutions. They made comments such as:

> '2 of those (beans) is 90p.'

> 'Beans and butter together makes £1.20, so two of each is £2.40.'

They repeatedly found the amounts of money left and when they found that they had made a mistake in their calculations they discussed why it did not work, as in this short exchange.

> '45 pence left.'
> 'Another tin of beans.'
> 'Oh, we're 10p over.'
> 'It must have been 35 pence.'

This simple situation served to stimulate an abundance of mental calculation and provided a natural forum for children to share their ideas and seek solutions.

Conclusion

Work using computers has much to offer for many aspects of learning mathematics, including the development of mental methods. Anybody who has seen children using a computer will have observed the strong motivation to be actively involved and how suitable software encourages purposeful discussion.

In this chapter we have considered how particular items of software allow pupils to do mental mathematics. Software which encourages discussion by presenting a sufficient challenge that demands thought and the sharing of ideas is likely to provide plenty of opportunity for working mentally, whereas drill and practice programs tend only to test what is already known, rather than encouraging wider discussion.

The limited availability of computers in many schools raises various issues, particularly what to do if only one computer is available in the classroom. Two or three children working at the computer may well be doing something different from the rest of the class, so how can the teacher know what is going on? It is not possible to see or hear everything, but the teacher can sample the occasional moment and, if talk is a feature of the classroom, reporting back may enable both children and teacher to realise what has been gained.

The way in which a problem is viewed may change because it is presented on the computer. The teachers who solved an equation by trial and improvement, rather than using the standard way which they teach, became involved because the computer produces answers quickly and allows many alternatives to be tried. Perhaps it is valuable to play with a problem in different ways before being introduced to a generalised method for solution. Often computer software enables mistakes to be erased quickly, so that, for example, the shopping bill problem on the spreadsheet is not a case of having to have the 'right answer' straight away, but an opportunity to test out ideas and amend calculations along the way.

Working with a program like TAKEHALF raises questions about how the computer can help children develop their powers of visualisation and prediction through the mental images they form. Turtle geometry using LOGO is particularly powerful in this respect. The use of graphical packages opens up a further area where mathematical ideas are presented in a powerful visual form and where mental images have an important role.

There are many ways in which the use of the computer in the mathematics classroom can provide opportunities for mental methods. Try out some software, watch and listen, and talk about what happens.

Software Selection

Brief additional details are given below of some of the items of software referred to in the chapter, together with the suppliers of each item. The software discussed represents only a very small selection from the wide range of programs which are available and which are useful for encouraging and exploring mental methods.

TRAINS
A number of carriages are offered which have to be filled with given numbers of people, aiming to fill the train with the target number.

TARGET
A game for two players (or two teams). Each player has the numbers 1 to 9 available, taking it in turns to add one of the numbers to the running total. Each number is available only once, the player wins when she or he obtains the target, or the other player overshoots.

TRAINS and TARGET appear in 'Number Games' by Anita Straker, which is obtainable from:

> Inner London Educational Computing Centre (ILECC),
> John Ruskin Street, LONDON, SE5 0PQ.

PREDICT
The user enters a set of numbers and the computer gives a result according to some rule. This is repeated until the user feels that she or he knows the rule and the computer then offers a test. This program is intended to help pupils look for the relationships between numbers.

FACTOR
The computer displays a list of numbers, the user chooses one and the computer acquires all of its factors. The user may only choose numbers which have factors in the list. The game continues until no factors are left and the computer acquires the remainder. The numbers are then totalled, the highest total wins.Unless you understand factors and primes the computer wins.

PREDICT, FACTOR and also TAKEHALF all appear in 'MicroSMILE: the first 31', obtainable from ILECC, as above.

ERGO, MONTY and COUNTER appear on two discs 'SLIMWAM1' and 'SLIMWAM 2' (Some Lessons In Mathematics With A Microcomputer), which are obtainable from:

> Association of Teachers of Mathematics (ATM),
> 7 Shaftesbury Street, Derby, DE3 8YB.

Conclusion:
Back to Basics

In our discussions of mental methods and in our attempts to present our thoughts for others in a written form, we have been acutely aware that it is difficult to consider the issues independently of the wider aspects of learning mathematics. The opportunities for mental activity of the kind we have been considering are present in most, if not all, of the varied activities that take place in the good mathematics classroom. They are not confined to those activities which are specifically designed with mental methods in mind. This raises issues of teacher awareness and teaching style, if the best use is to be made of incidental opportunities as they arise.

The importance of mental methods, at least in relation to number work, is widely recognised. The Cockcroft Report in 1982 drew attention to their important, but often neglected, role, which has subsequently been given particular emphasis in the National Curriculum for mathematics.

However, the means whereby mental skills can be extended and improved seems to have been given remarkably little serious consideration. The prevailing view, to judge from the evidence of most school text books, particularly at secondary level, is that practice obtained by working through sets of simple questions, commonly presented as a test, is all that is required. While this may be fine up to a point for those who are successful, it is likely to have positively harmful effects on those who find it difficult and often fail.

We feel that **all** children need ways of extending their mental skills through having opportunities to develop their own methods, to talk about them and to learn from each other and from their teachers by sharing and comparing ideas.

There are frequent suggestions that schools should give more attention to basic numeracy, and this is commonly equated with an ability to perform arithmetical operations in a mechanical way. It is some time since Michael Girling (in Mathematics Teaching, December 1977) gave us a provocative definition:

'Basic numeracy is the ability to use a four function calculator sensibly.'

The essence of 'sensible' use lies in choosing the most appropriate method for the task in hand. As Girling has suggested, mental methods will often be appropriate, and it is reassuring that evidence from the Calculator Aware Number (CAN) project suggests that, where children are encouraged to use calculators from an early age, they often choose to work mentally and achieve a surprising level of success.

Written methods, particularly the standard written algorithms, are, however, still often regarded as central to basic numeracy, in spite of all the evidence of confusion and misunderstanding that they cause for many children and of the fact that they are so little used in the 'real world', where calculators are used for all tasks that cannot be handled mentally. What is needed is some new definition of basic numeracy which encapsulates the idea of choosing, or devising, methods which are appropriate.

To be described as numerate a person has to have the ability to solve simple everyday problems involving number, by using effectively the knowledge and skills that they possess. The essence of problem solving is that the solver has to choose or devise a method to be used, and that requires, amongst other things, an ability to decide what calculations are needed and how best to do them. Perhaps, therefore, debate about numeracy should be directed much more towards the role of problem solving as the essential 'basic' skill. Attention is then focused on how to develop the abilities of choosing and devising appropriate strategies, which include strategies for doing calculations.

In this book we have tried to encourage a problem solving approach to learning mathematics by emphasising the importance of children discussing and refining their own methods, rather than simply relying on a limited selection of imposed standard methods. Such an approach is characterised by asking children to explain their own methods of working something out rather than by the teacher telling them how to do it. Total reliance on telling encourages dependence on the authority of the teacher and a belief that there is only one correct way of proceeding. It follows that the development of independent thinking, which is essential to effective problem solving and to improving mental skills, requires the teacher to avoid always telling children how to do things.

Encouraging the use of mental methods requires no elaborate or expensive resources, but it does require teachers to be alert to the possibilities of every situation, to be ever on the lookout for ways of stimulating children to think for themselves and to provide frequent opportunities for using and developing appropriate skills in a wide variety of contexts.

In conclusion, we should like to present a list that attempts to summarise the ideas and approaches which we have written about in seeking to encourage mental methods as a '**first resort**'. We suggest that activity to stimulate more effective and extensive use of mental methods should be characterised by:

★ mathematics as a **way of thinking** requiring active participation

★ **time** to think

★ a non-competitive, non-judgemental ethos

★ a high value placed on the ideas and contributions of the **children**

★ an emphasis on **understanding**

★ practice arising within a wide variety of situations

★ development of a wide range of strategies and methods to encourage a **flexible** approach to calculation

★ positive encouragement to consider **alternative** methods of looking at the same problem

★ a wide range of classroom activities extending to more than working with number

★ **talk** welcomed as a valuable means of clarifying and extending ideas and sharing them with others

★ encouragement of **independent** thinking

Bibliography

Books

Association of Teachers of Mathematics *Notes on Mathematics for Children* Cambridge University Press 1977

Association of Teachers of Mathematics *Mathematical Images* ATM, 1986

Buxton, L., *Do You Panic about Maths?* Heinemann, 1991

Cockcroft, W. H., *Mathematics Counts* HMSO, 1982

Department of Education and Science *Mathematics for Ages 5 to 16* DES, 1988

Department of Education and Science *Mathematics in the National Curriculum* HMSO, 1989

Department of Education and Science *Mathematics in the National Curriculum* HMSO, 1991

Dickson, L., Brown, M. and Gibson, O. *Children Learning Mathematics* Holt, 1984

Fielker, D. *Using Calculators with Upper Juniors* Association of Teachers of Mathematics, 1985

Fitzgerald, A. *New Technology and Mathematics in Employment* University of Birmingham, 1985

Ginsburg, H. *Children's Arithmetic: How They Learn It and How You Teach It* Austin, Texas, 1977

Hart, K. (editor) *Children's Understanding of Mathematics: 11-16* John Murray, 1981

HMI *Mathematics from 5 to 16* HMSO, 1985

HMI *Aspects of Primary Education: The Teaching and Learning of Mathematics* HMSO, 1989

Holt, J. *How Children Fail* Penguin 1984

Hughes, M. *Children and Number* Basil Blackwell, 1986

Mathematical Association *Maths Talk* Stanley Thornes, 1987

National Curriculum Council *Mathematics: Non-Statutory Guidance* NCC, 1989

School Examinations and Asssessment Council *APU Mathematics Monitoring 1984-88 (Phase 2) A Summary of Findings, Conclusions and Implications* SEAC, 1990

Shuard, H., Walsh, A., Goodwin, J. and Worcester, V. *Calculators, Children and Mathematics* Simon and Schuster, 1991

Articles in Mathematics in School

Aze, Ian *More on Mental Methods in Mathematics* Volume 17, No. 2, March 1988

Duffin, Janet *Written Algorithms* Volume 20, No. 4, September 1991

French, Doug *Mental Methods in Mathematics* Volume 16, No. 2, March 1987

Jones, Pamela *Mental Mathematics Moves Ahead* Volume 17, No. 3, May 1988

Plunkett, Stuart *Decomposition and All That Rot* Volume 8, No. 3, May 1979

Smith, Robert *What's Going On in Their Heads?* Volume 18, No. 5, November 1989

Thompson, Ian *SATisfactory Progress* Volume 20, No. 5, November 1991

Other Articles

Duffin, Janet *Mathematics for the Nineties: A Calculator Aware Number Curriculum* Mathematics Teaching, No. 136, September 1991

Girling, Michael *Towards a Definition of Basic Numeracy* Mathematics Teaching, No. 81, December 1977

McIntosh, Alistair *When Will They Ever Learn?* Forum, Volume 19, No. 3, Summer 1977 (reprinted in Mathematics Teaching, No. 86, March 1979)

McIntosh, Alistair *Mental Mathematics — Some Suggestions* Mathematics Teaching, No. 91, June 1980

Thompson, Ian *Mental Efficiency* Times Educational Supplement, 5th May, 1989